Health Care Reform Terms

Second Edition

An explanatory glossary of words, phrases, & acronyms used in today's U.S. "health care reform" movement.

Vergil N. Slee, MD
Debora A. Slee, JD

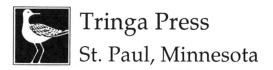

Tringa Press
St. Paul, Minnesota

Tringa Press
P.O. Box 8181
St. Paul, MN 55108
612-222-7476

Printed in the United States of America.

96 95 94   9 8 7 6 5 4 3 2

Preface & Caveat

"Health Care Reform" is a term in the spotlight, and it has brought many more new terms along with it This book was initially prepared at the request of Estes Park Institute to help elucidate the terminology being used in the health care reform discussions in order to facilitate communication and better decision-making.

This book is now in its second edition, with approximately 300 terms added, and others revised, since the first edition of the book was published last fall.

The need for some sort of reference has been great, because of the rapidity of change in terminology and the fact that different terms mean different things to different people. For example, some of the early proposals referred to an institution called the "health insurance purchasing cooperative (HIPC)." But this was replaced with "health plan purchasing cooperative (HPPC)," and is now called "health alliance (HA)." Whether it will remain "HA," or change again, no one can predict.

This "moving target" of terminology, which obviously breeds confusion, may suit the purposes of some, but it does not promote thoughtful consideration of the problems in health care which need to be addressed and the solutions being proposed.

Such changes may reflect changes in the concept. But they may also reflect desires to claim ownership. In view of examples like the above, it makes sense to challenge speakers and writers as to the precise meaning of the terms as they are using them.

April 1994

About the Authors

Vergil N. Slee, MD, MPH, is Chairman of the Board of the Health Commons Institute and President Emeritus of the Commission on Professional and Hospital Activities (CPHA). He pioneered the Professional Activity Study (PAS) and founded CPHA, and was president of the Council on Clinical Classifications which, with the U.S. National Center for Health Statistics, created the *Clinical Modification* of the *International Classification of Diseases, Ninth Revision (ICD-9-CM)*. Dr. Slee has served for over twenty-five years as a member of the faculty of Estes Park Institute (EPI), which presents national conferences for hospital trustees, administrators, and medical staff officers, and their spouses, on emerging health care issues. He is a Fellow of the American College of Physicians, a Fellow of the American Public Health Association, and an Honorary Fellow of the American College of Healthcare Executives.

Debora A. Slee, JD, is an attorney and writer with experience in health care law and hospital quality management. She is contributing author to *The Law of Hospital and Health Care Administration, Second Edition,* by Arthur F. Southwick, and coauthor of *Health Care Terms, Second Edition.*

Overview

"Health care reform" is the expression used to include all the efforts to solve the problems of:

COST: Costs of health care are seen as too high and still rising. The United States spends a much larger share of the gross domestic product on health care than any other country and, critics say, our health doesn't reflect the difference. Health care costs, which must be covered by the prices of our products and our taxes, are seen as a major reason that the United States is losing its competitive position in the world market.

WASTE: The media are full of stories about waste, unnecessary care, and fraud. Even if not all of this attention is warranted, it provides fuel for the reform movement.

EQUITY: Inequities among regions of the country, between rural and urban settings, among ethnic groups, and among socioeconomic groups, in access to and quality of both preventive and curative services, are widely reported.

ACCESS: There is increasing concern not only with access in its traditional meaning, having to do with the ability of the individual to physically get to and utilize health care facilities, but also with "access" meaning eligibility for (access to) insurance benefits. A person who has an income too high to qualify for Medicaid in a given state, for example, does not have access to Medicaid benefits.

ACCOUNTABILITY: Society is demanding that health care providers show evidence as to the quality of care they deliver, and also their stewardship of resources.

QUALITY: Care is alleged to be of variable quality from place to place and from provider to provider. And there are charges and fears that cost containment is tantamount to lowering quality.

PREVENTION: There is a growing recognition that prevention, of illnesses and injuries, as well as of the progression of illness, saves
money. Yet preventive services are absent from most health insurance policies and many health care plans.

SECURITY: People lose their health insurance when they change
jobs, so they are sometimes "locked in" to their employment. Some
cannot obtain health insurance. And they are concerned that health
care will destroy them financially. A stated goal of health care reform is that people will never lose their insurance, and that health
care will not bankrupt individuals.

WHY NOW?

In addition to the above concerns to the American people, other
changes are occurring today in our society at the personal level
which provide impetus to make fundamental changes in our health
care system. These are "paradigm shifts" in the way an increasing
number of people think about being and staying healthy, and about
their relationships with their health care providers. Several significant shifts are:

1. From the view that health care providers are there to provide
"health care," to the view that "health" rather than "health care" is
their goal.

2. From the view that knowledge processing is limited to the human
mind, plus "paper and pencil," to the view that knowledge processing can be successfully extended through the use of computer technology.

3. From the view that the physician should retain the "paternal" role
of caring and making decisions for the patient, to the view that empowered patients are competent to collaborate in their own health
care and that, in fact, many wish to and can *direct* their own care.

4. From the view that the government is responsible for the health of
the community, to the view that the community itself is responsible.

WHAT ARE THE GREATEST EFFECTS EXPECTED FROM "REFORM"?

COST CONTROLS will be imposed on both

- Physicians
- Hospitals

REGULATION will be increased on

- Hospital operations
- Physician's care of patients (the growing number of "guidelines" and "critical paths" seems sure to be followed by their being mandated).

LIMITED FREEDOM will be given patients and employers as to where and how they may obtain health care.

LESS MONEY will be available through government and health care benefits, and, unless local initiative intervenes, what money there is almost certainly will be administered through some mechanisms outside the community, mechanisms which probably will not be welcomed by the local community and its health care providers.

WHAT IS BEING PROPOSED?

Several approaches are being suggested for health care reform; for example, patterning our system on those of certain states or nations (see, for example, the *Canadian-style system, German-style system,* and the plans discussed under *Hawaii, Minnesota,* and *Oregon*). Most "in the news" is President Clinton's proposal, embodied in the Health Security Act. That plan embraces the concept of **MANAGED COMPETITION**, at least four elements of which seem to be emerging:

1. **PURCHASER:** Most health care will be purchased through either a major employer with good purchasing power or through a new kind of entity, a purchasing agent called a **health alliance (HA)**, established locally primarily to serve as a "sponsor" for the community's small employers and individuals. (Of course, larger employers could join the HA if they wished.)

2. **PROVIDER:** Each purchaser of health care will be required to be given a choice among government-approved or licensed **"accountable health plans (AHPs)."** An essential element of an AHP is that it provides (1) an insurance plan, and (2) both physician and hospi-

tal care (and perhaps long-term care and other health care benefits)
under a single administration and premium. That would mean that
there would have to be at least two AHPs available in any community. (Some discussions suggest that rural communities would be
handled differently.)

3. **GLOBAL BUDGETING:** Stated to be a limit on total health care
   spending for a given unit of population, taking into account all
   sources of funds. It is not clear how the information as to the total
   spending data are to be obtained or the **"cap"** will be enforced, but
   suggestions are that there will be caps on (1) employers expenditures, based on payroll, (2) individual expenditures for insurance,
   based on income, (3) institutional budgets' "core spending," and (4)
   personal out-of-pocket expenditures. The addition of global budgeting to the picture means "managed competition under a cap."

4. **QUALITY OF CARE** will increasingly be measured, with an emphasis on **"outcomes."** The quality will be publicized, and taken
   into account by the sponsors and the consumers in their selection of
   an AHP. Consumers will be given "report cards" on their providers.

HOW IS THE REFORM PROCESS BEING APPROACHED?

President Clinton's Task Force on National Health Reform has been
widely discussed in the media. A great many meetings have been
held with participation by the American people, all categories of
health care providers, the business community, and all levels of government; more than 1,500 meetings involving more than 1,150
groups. The product was the Health Security Act (HSA), introduced in October 1993.

Local and state efforts are also going forward at a rapid pace. One
state which has had a good deal of attention is Oregon, which
started with development of consensus among its citizens, using a
design process which followed a logical sequence, posing and answering four questions as to the goals of the reform and its "shape."
Each question had to be answered before the subsequent questions
could be productively considered. The questions:

1. What is the overall goal of reform? There were two choices: It is to
   improve "health" or to provide "health care."

2. Who is to be covered? The choices are all persons ("universal coverage") or some subset of the population.

3. What are to be the benefits? Most discussions assume that there will be a "basic benefit package" as the core or floor which will be available to all covered persons. (A basic package does not preclude optional "add-ons" to supplement the basic package.) Oregon's approach to defining benefits was unique (see *Oregon plan*).

4. How will financing be accomplished? Options include employer mandate, which would cover the employed population; formation of other groups (such as health alliances (HAs)), at least for purposes of insurance purchase; relying on personal responsibility; federal or state subsidy of or outright provision of the insurance; and other mechanisms.

WHAT IS BEING DONE?

About a dozen bills have now been introduced in Congress; several of them comprise the "Health Security Act." Others offer counter-proposals, usually for less extensive changes than the President's plan. (See the listings under *Health Security Act, HR,* and *S* for the specific bills.)

An increasing number of states have adopted reform legislation of their own, while others have bills pending.

Dominant features of the developing scene are that:

1. The entire population will one day be served by "integrated health systems" or "integrated health networks"; stand-alone hospitals and solo practitioners are vanishing breeds.

2. Physician-hospital organizations (PHOs) will be developed in virtually every community so that a single entity can provide both physician and hospital care (vertically integrated systems); patients and other purchasers want "one-stop shopping" with prices stated in advance.

3. Capitation is likely to replace fee-for-service as the usual method of paying for both physician and hospital services.

4. Quality management will be built into the system, so that providers are accountable for both the quality and cost-effectiveness of their care.

A

AAFP: See *American Academy of Family Physicians.*

AAHC: See *American Association of Healthcare Consultants.*

abuse: The improper or excessive use of health care products and services. Abuse may result from excessive (unnecessary) use of diagnostic tests, unnecessary surgical and other procedures, and so forth. Abuse may be either intentional or unintentional, and may or may not be illegal.

The laws governing Medicare, for example, make certain referral arrangements illegal because they create opportunity for abuse, even though there may be no actual abuse or intent to abuse. See *fraud and abuse.*

accelerated death benefit: Any amount paid to an individual under a life insurance contract on the life of an insured who is a terminally ill individual. This benefit is treated under *HR 3704* as an amount paid by reason of the death of such insured.

access (1): Physical access. Traditionally, access means the ability of patients to simply "get into" and utilize health care facilities, hence the term "barrier-free access."

access (2): In health care reform discussions, access usually means eligibility for (access to) insurance benefits, since lack of insurance can be a formidable barrier to health care. Individuals who are above a given state's definition of the poverty level for qualification for Medicaid are said to be denied access. In 1990, for example, when the federal poverty threshold was $13,356, access was very different in a state which had its Medicaid threshold at $3,000 (family income above this amount disqualifies the family for Medicaid) than in a state where the threshold was $10,000. Thus, an unemployed or employed low income person who cannot be insured through an employer, might not qualify for public assistance, either.

accountability: The obligation to provide, to all concerned, the evidence needed to: (1) establish confidence that the task or duty for which one is responsible is being or has been performed; and (2) describe the manner in which that task is being or has been carried out. When accountability has been fulfilled, the authority which delegated the responsibility can be satisfied by evidence (rather than simply assertion) that the duties or tasks which have been delegated are being or have been adequately performed.

Accountability must be defined in conjunction with responsibility. An individual or organization has responsibility (that is to say, an obligation) because some individual or body with authority has granted or delegated that responsibility. Failure to carry out the responsibility carries with it liability. A responsible party is entitled to delegate duties, that is, to get help in carrying out the obligation, but not to delegate the responsibility itself. The responsible party, therefore, must have reasonable ground on which he can render account (be accountable) for the duties which have been delegated. So the delegation of duties, as a matter of law, carries with it the requirement of accountability to the source of the delegation of the duties.

A hospital, for example, is delegated certain duties by "society," by government. For this purpose, the hospital's responsibility is accepted and held by its governing body. The governing body must render account for its performance (it holds accountability) to society, through specific reporting mechanisms, voluntary efforts to provide society evidence of its performance, and defending itself against liability suits. In turn the governing body delegates tasks to the chief executive officer (CEO) and demands accounting from that individual; the CEO, in turn, delegates tasks to departmental heads and demands accountability from them.

Similarly, the governing body gives the medical staff organization (MSO) duties, for example, with respect to the credentialing of applicants for medical staff membership. The MSO incurs, along with the duty, the obligation of accountability--it must provide the evidence needed to establish the governing body's confidence that it, the MSO, has indeed performed the task, and the evidence must be presented in enough detail to permit the governing body to assess the quality of performance of the duty.

accountable health partnership (AHP): See *accountable health plan.*

accountable health plan (AHP): A health care organization or network which provides both health insurance services and health care is often called a health plan (or health care plan). Some current health care reform proposals revolve around such organizations, which would be accountable for meeting yet-to-be-established federal requirements for providing certain standardized health services. Under *HR 3222,* an accountable health plan is one registered with the *Health Care Standards Commission (Commission).* Synonym(s): accountable health partnership (AHP), approved health plan (AHP).
See also *health care plan.*

accrediting organization: Under *HR 3704,* must " . . . i) exist for the primary purpose of accrediting coordinated care organizations; ii) be governed by a group of individuals representing health care providers, purchasers, regulators, and consumers (a minority of which shall be representatives of health care providers); iii) have substantial experience in accrediting coordinated care organizations, including an organization's internal quality assurance program; iv) be independent of health care providers or associations of health care providers; v) be a nonprofit organization; and vi) have an accreditation process which meets requirements specified by the Secretary [of Health and Human Services]." Note: This would appear to disqualify the Joint Commission on Accreditation of Healthcare Organizations (JCAHO).

actuary: A specialized statistician whose work is to estimate risks as, for example, in the setting of insurance premiums (see *risk (1).*

acute care: Care for short-term patients.

ADA: See *Americans with Disabilities Act*.

ADC: See *Aid to Families with Dependent Children*.

ADF: See *administrative determination of fault* under *alternative dispute resolution*.

ADFS: See *alternative delivery and financing system*.

administrative determination of fault (ADF):   See *alternative dispute resolution*.

Administrator for Health Care Policy and Research: See *Agency for Health Care Policy and Research (AHCPR)*.

admission: Formal acceptance of a patient by a hospital or other health care institution or agency in order to provide care or services. See also *readmission*.

ADR: See *alternative dispute resolution*.

ADR system: See *federal alternative dispute resolution system*.

ADS: See *alternative delivery system*.

advance directive: A statement executed by a person while of sound mind as to that person's wishes about the use of medical interventions for himself in case of the loss of his own decision-making capacity. A number of forms of advance directives have been proposed and are used; some are described below. See also *Patient Self-Determination Act (PSDA), value history,* and *value inventory*.

   Under *HR 3704*, "An advance directive that fails to meet the formalities of execution, form, or language required by State law shall be given effect to the extent that the treating health care provider in good faith believes that such directive constitutes a reliable expression of the wishes of the individual executing such directive concerning such individual's health care . . . Nothing . . . may be construed to authorize the administration, withholding, or withdrawal of health care otherwise prohibited by the laws of the State."

durable power of attorney: A power of attorney which remains (or becomes) effective when the principal becomes incompetent to act for herself. It should be noted that in most states, even an agent with a durable power of attorney cannot make medical treatment decisions for an incompetent patient, unless state law provides that she can or a court has given her specific authority.

health care proxy: A document which authorizes a designated person to make health care decisions in the event that the signer is incapable of making those decisions. State law governs whether such a document is valid, how it must be created, and to what extent the proxy is authorized to make health care decisions. For example, a proxy may not be able to consent to electroconvulsive therapy or sterilization.

instructional advance directive (IAD): An *advance directive* in which an attempt is made to allow the person executing the directive to record quite specifically those interventions which are not to be attempted in case of the loss of the person's own decision-making capacity.

> **The Medical Directive**: An *instructional advance directive* document published in the *New England Journal of Medicine* in 1989 which has been made available to the lay public. The Medical Directive describes four clinical scenarios, each of which affects the patient's own decision-making capacity, and then lists a series of medical diagnostic or therapeutic interventions. The person who completes the document checks off whether he would choose the interventions in the case of each of the scenarios. The completed document is interpreted as an advance directive for the person who completes it.

living will: A will concerning the life of the individual executing the will, in contrast with the usual "last will and testament" in which the subject matter is the disposition of property (this could be thought of as a "property will") and custody of minor children. In many states, individuals may execute "living wills" concerning the circumstances under which they wish to refuse, or discontinue the use of, life-support measures administered to themselves should they become *incompetent (1)*. Living will statutes (also known as *right to die* laws or *natural death acts*) govern the execution and enforcement procedures for living wills. At least one state (New Hampshire) calls the living will a "terminal care document."

The "life-sustaining procedures act," proposed by the National Conference of Commissioners on Uniform State Laws, suggests the following language for a living will: "If I should have an incurable or irreversible condition that will cause my death within a relatively short time, and if I am unable to make decisions regarding my medical treatment, I direct my attending physician to withhold or withdraw procedures that merely prolong the dying process and are not necessary to my comfort or to alleviate pain."

adverse change in health outcome: Under *HR 3222*, "a biological or psychological decremental change in a health status or if the original endowment for a feature lies outside the normal range."

adverse selection: A situation in which patients with greater than average need for medical and hospital care enroll in a *prepaid health plan* in greater numbers than they occur in a cross-section of the population. A plan which somehow encouraged or allowed people to sign up when they were already ill would suffer from adverse selection. *Community rating* (see *rating*) would not only even out the premiums for health insurance by spreading the risk over a broad base, it also would reduce the chances that a group (community) would be so small as to permit serious adverse selection.

advocacy: Attempting to persuade others of the rightness of a cause, or of a point of view on an issue. Such educational efforts--for example, health education--are increasingly undertaken by hospitals and other *nonprofit* organizations, but if they are addressed at passing or defeating legislation, they may be classified as *lobbying* and therefore endanger the organization's *tax-exempt* status.

AFDC: See *Aid to Families with Dependent Children.*

affiliation: Any one of a number of arrangements among providers outlining their relationships and their individual responsibilities. The relationships are contained in documents which range from broad letters of intent to detailed contracts. In the past, such arrangements were often called alliances, but this term has been preempted in the health care reform movement by proposals for specific organizations labelled "health care alliances," which are often referred to merely as "alliances." See *alliance (2).*

Affordable Health Care Now Act of 1993: See *HR 3080.*

AFS: See *alternative financing system.*

agency: Administrative agency. A part of state or federal government, created by the legislature, which has specific administrative duties and functions, often including regulation of a profession or industry. A state board of medical examiners, for example, is an administrative agency. There is a body of law (administrative law) which governs the powers of administrative agencies, the process of agency decision-making, and the procedures by which a party dissatisfied with a decision of an agency can challenge it. Ordinarily, any person who wishes to contest an administrative agency decision must go through all of the channels of appeal within the agency before challenging the decision in the courts.

Agency for Clinical Evaluations: Under *HR 3704,* the Secretary [of Health and Human Services] is to examine the feasibility of consolidating the responsibilities, insofar as such responsibilities relate to clinical evaluations, of 4 agencies: (1) the Agency for Health Care Policy and Research (AHCPR), (2) the National Center for Health Statistics (NCHS), (3) the Office of Medical Applications Research at the National Institutes of Health, and (4) the Office of Research and Demonstrations of the Health Care Financing Administration (HCFA).

Agency for Health Care Policy and Research (AHCPR): A component of the Public Health Service (PHS), which is in turn a component of the Department of Health and Human Services (DHHS). Among its functions is the dissemination of information about the assessment of health technology. See *Office of Health Technology Assessment (OHTA).*

    The *Health Security Act (HSA)* provides that the Administrator for Health Care Policy and Research receive guidance from the *National Quality Management Council (NQMC)* and the *National Quality Consortium (NQC)* on matters such as clinical practice guidelines (see *guidelines (2)*), *national measures of quality performance (NMQP),* and research priorities.

AHA: See *American Hospital Association.*

AHCPR: See *Agency for Health Care Policy and Research.*

AHP: Accountable health partnership, accountable health plan, approved health plan. See *accountable health plan.*

AHSA: See *American Health Security Act.*

Aid to Families with Dependent Children (ADC, AFDC): A federally financed program for single-parent families, designed to provide essential needs and services for single parents who cannot, without this assistance, take proper care of the children.

all-payer plan: A payment policy under which the same payment method is applied to patients of all *payers.* Today, the term "all-payer plan" really means applying the *prospective payment system (PPS)* to all patients, rather than Medicare patients only. (Medicare patients are the only patients to which the PPS applies under the present federal regulations.)

All-Payer Health Care Fraud and Abuse Control Account: Under the *Health Security Act (HSA),* an account to be set up by the federal Treasury, into which would be deposited fines, penalties, assessments, and property forfeitures for "federal health care offenses," defined in the Act. It could also accept gifts and bequests. The funds in the account would be used without appropriation by both the Secretary of Health and Human Services (HHS) and the Attorney General for fraud and abuse control program activities, including investigations, prosecutions, audits, and inspections.

alliance (1): In common usage, any one of a variety of collaborative arrangements among individuals or institutions. In the past, hospitals have formed alliances or affiliations, for example, between those furnishing primary, secondary, and tertiary care. The term "alliance" for this type of arrangement should be used carefully in the face of the adoption in the *Health Security Act* of the term *health alliances,* which has a specific meaning, and may be referred to as simply "alliance" or "regional alliance" or "corporate alliance.""

alliance (2): In the *Health Security Act (HSA),* the term *health alliance* has been adopted to replace a variety of terms used in earlier discussions to label the "health insurance purchasing" bodies. Used alone, "alliance" is likely to have this meaning.

allocation of risk mechanism: Under *HR 3080,* a " . . . mechanism under which uninsurable small employers would be equitably assigned among insurers offering health insurance plans to small employers."

ALOS: See *average length of stay.*

alternative: One of two or more feasible ways of doing something. Often the term is used to mean new or different from what has been done before. The term is being used increasingly in health care, for example, in connection with financing methods and the organization of services.

alternative delivery and financing system (ADFS): A general term which covers any kind of *alternative* organizational arrangement for the delivery of health care, such as a *health maintenance organization (HMO),* in which payment for physician services is other than *fee-for-service (FFS).* Thus, an

ADFS is a combination of an *alternative delivery system (2) (ADS)* and an *alternative financing system (AFS)*.

alternative delivery mode: See *alternative delivery system (ADS)*.

alternative delivery system (1) (ADS): An *alternative* to traditional inpatient care, such as substitution of *ambulatory care, home health care, hospice,* or *same-day surgery.* Synonym(s): alternative delivery mode.

alternative delivery system (2) (ADS): An *alternative* to the traditional arrangements of health care providers into solo practice or group practice. Examples include the *independent physician association (IPA), preferred provider organization (PPO), health maintenance organization (HMO),* and *health care organization (HCO).* The method of purchase of service or payment of physicians *(fee-for-service (FFS)* or *capitation,* for example) does not govern the term in this usage.

alternative dispute resolution (ADR): Methods of settling claims and disagreements other than by the traditional method--a lawsuit. Alternatives proposed for resolving *malpractice* claims include:

administrative determination of fault (ADF): A proposed method of alternative dispute resolution combining features of a *compensation fund* and *arbitration.* Claims would be filed with a designated agency which would determine whether or not there were negligence and, if there were, the claimant would be paid from a fund. Provision would be made for administrative appeal.

arbitration: When used as a method of alternative dispute resolution, providers and patients would agree in advance to have any disputes handled by *arbitration* rather than going to court.

compensation fund: A fund into which insurers, practitioners, and facilities would deposit moneys to be used to compensate anyone "injured in the course of receiving health care services, regardless of whether the provider or professional was negligent."

early offer: A form of alternative dispute resolution in which the practitioner or provider could, in cases of injury, make an offer which, if accepted, would preclude certain court actions and result in prompt payment for costs (but not for pain and suffering). See *patient's compensation* under *compensation.*

alternative dispute resolution system: See *federal alternative dispute resolution system.*

alternative financing system (AFS): An *alternative* to the *fee-for-service (FFS)* payment system, such as a *health care organization (HCO), health maintenance organization (HMO),* or *competitive medical plan (CMP)* in which some other mechanism, usually *capitation,* is the method of payment to the organization and sometimes to the physician.

AMA: See *American Medical Association.*

ambulatory care: Care provided to a patient without *hospitalization.*

ambulatory care system: Although people use this phrase, such as in "the U.S. ambulatory care system," it has no specific meaning.

ambulatory training sites: Under *HR 3704*, " . . . includes, but is not limited to, health maintenance organizations, federally qualified health centers, community health centers, migrant health centers, rural health clinics, nursing homes, hospice, and other community-based providers, including private practices."

ambulatory visit group (AVG): A counterpart of the *diagnosis related group (DRG) classification (1)*, but designed for use for *ambulatory care* rather than hospital care. Patients, as in DRGs, undergo *classification (2)* into diagnosis groups (in this case, AVGs rather than DRGs) for which a predetermined or prenegotiated fee can be established.

American Academy of Family Physicians (AAFP): A national association of specialists in family practice (primary care physicians), with about 60,000 members.

American Association of Healthcare Consultants (AAHC): A national organization whose membership is restricted to those health care consultants who meet written and oral examinations and peer review requirements. Members are entitled to fellowship, and may use "FAAHC" after their names.

American Health Security Act (AHSA): A health reform bill introduced to Congress (S 491) by Senator Wellstone. The proposal, a *single-payer plan*, emphasizes universal access, continuous coverage, freedom of choice for the individual, affordability, comprehensive benefits (including mental health services), state administration, consumer accountability, and emphasis on primary care.

American Hospital Association (AHA): The national association of hospitals in the U.S. Other health care organizations and individuals may also hold membership. In addition to membership activities, it maintains a major reference library of hospital literature, and publishes a number of titles, including the magazine, *Hospitals*, and two standard annual reference volumes, *Hospital Statistics* and *Guide to the Health Care Field*. American Hospital Association, 840 North Lake Shore Drive, Chicago, IL 60611-2431. Telephone 312-280-6000.

American Hospital System: Although this term is often used, there really is no such thing as the "American Hospital System," except that the nation's hospitals and other health care facilities, along with health professionals and allied health professionals, do make up an informal network across the country through which care is provided. The "American Hospital System" simply means what actually exists--community hospitals, university hospitals, nonprofit hospitals, investor-owned hospitals, government hospitals, and the like.

American Medical Association (AMA): The major national association of physicians in the U.S. All physicians who have the degree Doctor of Medicine (MD) are eligible for membership.

Americans with Disabilities Act (ADA): A federal law which prohibits discrimination against persons with physical or mental disabilities by private sector service providers, employers, and state and local governments. The law requires reasonable accommodation and equal opportunity for persons with disabilities. It became effective in 1992. One aspect of the law is that it prohibits employers from discriminating on the basis of disability in the provision of health insurance to their employees.

ancillary services: Hospitals define this as services other than room and board. In a hospital, nursing services are included as part of "room and board"; since normal nursing services are not billed for separately, they are not ancillary services.

The *Oregon plan* defines ancillary services as those services which are considered to be integral to successful treatment of a condition. Examples given are hospital services, laboratory services, radiation therapy, prescription drugs, medical transportation, rehabilitation, maternity case management, and hospice services. See also *comfort care.*

anhedonia: The absence of fun.

anti-dumping law: A law which prohibits the transfer or discharge of patients for financial rather than medical reasons. See *dumping* and *Consolidated Omnibus Budget Reconciliation Act of 1985 (COBRA).*

antikickback law: Sometimes used to refer to the Medicare fraud and abuse laws, which prohibit, among other things, paying or receiving "kickbacks" for referral of Medicare patients. See *fraud and abuse.*

antitrust: That branch of law which seeks to prevent monopolies and unfair competition. A "trust" was originally a combination of several corporations (each maintaining its separate identity) to eliminate competition, control prices, and the like. The term "antitrust" now broadly covers any activity (or conspiracy) to eliminate competition and control the marketplace. It includes actions which unreasonably restrain trade. Such activities are illegal, and severe penalties are imposed by antitrust laws. For example, the trust may be broken up (divested), and anyone who suffers injury to their business or property as a result of the combination or conspiracy may collect treble damages. Federal antitrust laws (principally the Sherman Act of 1890, the Clayton Act of 1914, and the Federal Trade Commission Act of 1914) apply to companies doing business in interstate commerce. Many states also have antitrust laws.

Antitrust problems may arise for hospitals when they place limitations on medical staff membership, for example, or when several hospitals seek to combine services. Careful legal guidance is required in any area in which a hospital's actions may affect competition or regulate prices.

Antitrust issues are of concern in health care reform because of the fear that innovative approaches to health care organization and delivery of service may be deemed to be in violation of the antitrust regulations. Serious consideration is being given to amending the laws or providing for exceptions in order to stimulate and facilitate experimentation, and avoid unnecessary duplication of services.

appropriate certifying authority: Under *HR 3704*, the agency in a State with a qualified health plan certifying program, the State commissioner or superintendent of insurance (or equivalent authority), or the Secretary of Health and Human Services.

appropriateness: A term used in connection with review of care to indicate whether the measures taken were proper under the circumstances, and whether it would have been proper to have taken other measures under the circumstances.

approved health plan (AHP): See *accountable health plan*.

approved research trial: Under *HR 3222*, a trial " . . . approved by the Secretary of Health and Human Services . . . or by the National Institutes of Health, the Food and Drug Administration . . . the Department of Veterans Affairs, or by a qualified nongovernmental research entity . . . "

arbitration: A method of resolving disputes without use of the courts. A single *arbitrator* or panel of arbitrators is chosen by the parties to hear the case, and the parties agree to be bound by the arbitrators' decision. The arbitrator's decision is usually final; a court will not overrule it unless there was fraud or partiality involved. See also *alternative dispute resolution*.

area wage adjustment: A component of the payment formula under the *prospective payment system (PPS)* to allow for differences in wage scales in different parts of the country.

assignment (of benefits): A voluntary decision by the *beneficiary* to have insurance *benefits* paid directly to the *provider* rather than to the beneficiary himself. The act requires the signing of a form for the purpose. The provider is not usually obligated to accept an assignment of benefits; it may refuse and instead require the beneficiary to handle the collection procedure. Conversely, the provider may insist on assignment in order to protect its revenue; if the provider accepts the assignment, it ordinarily assumes responsibility for the collection paperwork. See also *balance billing* and *mandatory assignment*.

at risk: Under *HR 3080*, an entity is at risk " . . . when it is paid a fixed amount for providing or arranging for the provision of specified health care items and services . . . and is liable for all or part of the cost of furnishing such items . . . regardless of whether or the extent to which such cost exceeds the fixed payment."

AVG: See *ambulatory visit group*.

B

balance billing: The practice of physicians to charge a patient the balance of charges when the patient's insurance (or other third party payer) will not pay the entire charge. For example, when Medicare will pay the physician only 80% of her or his usual fee for a given service, the physician sometimes "balance bills" the patient, who then has to pay the balance. A practitioner who has agreed to accept assignment as payment in full cannot balance bill the patient. See also *assignment* and *mandatory assignment*.

bare-bones health plan: A no-frills health care plan or health care insurance policy with limited coverage, large deductibles and copayments, and low policy limits. Designed to be affordable to small businesses.

base premium rate: Under *HR 3080*, the lowest premium rate for a given *class of business*.

base unit: A *procedure* or *service* used in developing a relative value scale (RVS). See *relative value scale (RVS)*.

base year Medicare costs: A hospital's costs for the base year from which computations are made in the Medicare payment formula. The base year is, by definition, always several years behind the present, and its costs are those as determined according to the federal regulations for cost allocations.

BC: See *Blue Cross*.

BC/BS: See *Blue Cross and Blue Shield*.

BCBSA: See *Blue Cross and Blue Shield Association*.

bed pan mutual: A slang term for a physician-owned *professional liability insurance* company.

BEDS Board: See *Benefits, Evaluations, and Data Standards Board*.

behavior offset: A overall percentage decrease in physician fees to be paid by Medicare during the period of transition to the *resource based relative value scale (RBRVS)*. The assumption is made by the Health Care Financing Administration (HCFA) that physicians will attempt to adjust to the RBRVS (which will reduce physician fees for certain services) by increasing their volume of services, i.e., by changing their behavior. Thus the fee reduction to counter this and keep the total Medicare spending for physician services from increasing is termed by HCFA a "behavior offset." The process of adopting the RBRVS also has a "volume adjustment" aimed at the same goal, and a great deal of opposition has developed in Congress as well as among physicians against the additional behavior offset.

benchmark: Something which serves as a standard against which other things can be measured.

beneficiary: The person entitled to *benefits* from insurance or some other health care financing program, such as Medicare--the person "insured" as contrasted with the owner of the policy, for example.

benchmarking: A system whereby health care assessment undertakes to measure its performance against "best practice" standards. Best practice standards can reflect: (1) Evidence-based medical practice. This is practice supported by current investigative studies of like patient populations. (2)

Knowledge-based systems. These are systems wherein data elements are summarized into patterns (information) and that information is displayed against patterns derived from larger (regional or national) data bases (i.e. comparison of pattern of transluminal coronary artery angioplasty mortality and morbidity against state patterns). Explicit in benchmarking is movement away from anecdotal and single-practitioner experience based practice: "I had a patient once who . . . "

benefit package: The array or set of *benefits* included in or provided by a given insurance "policy." The term is widely heard in the health care reform discussions; one does not hear it used in connection with automobile insurance, for example. Several specific types of benefit package are mentioned:

basic benefit package: A *standard benefit package* which contains the services which must be the *least* which can be provided to any insured individual. Such a package would be the "floor" under the health benefits given to any individual. States, insurance companies, employers, or others could offer or provide additional benefits at their discretion. Health care reform discussions assume the existence of such a package. Also called "core benefit package" or "benchmark benefit package."

benchmark benefit package: See *basic benefit package*.

catastrophic benefit package: A benefit package required of each qualified health plan by *HR 3704*.

comprehensive benefit package: The term used in the *Health Security Act (HSA)* for the *basic benefit package* to which Americans would be guaranteed access. The package is to include items and services under 18 headings: (1) hospital services; (2) services of health professionals; (3) emergency and ambulatory medical and surgical services; (4) clinical preventive services; (5) mental health and substance abuse services; (6) family planning services and services for pregnant women; (7) hospice care; (8) home health care; (9) extended care services; (10) ambulance services; (11) outpatient laboratory, radiology, and diagnostic services; (12) outpatient prescription drugs and biologicals; (13) outpatient rehabilitation services; (14) durable medical equipment and prosthetic and orthotic devices; (15) vision care; (16) dental care; (17) health education classes; and (18) investigational treatments.

core benefit package: See *basic benefit package*.

defined benefit package: See *standard benefit package*.

Medicare benefit package: The federal government defines a *basic benefit package* for Medicare beneficiaries at the federal level for those for whom it provides coverage, and Medicare benefits are thus uniform throughout the country. *Medicaid* benefit packages, on the other hand, are determined by each state.

standard benefit package: A uniform (usually mandated) package of health insurance or health plan benefits. The purposes of standard benefit packages are to permit purchasers to compare among plans as to price and to prevent risk selection by the plans (see *risk (1)*). For true plan comparison, there must also be standard definitions of benefits; see *benefits*.

Under *HR 3704*, for example, " . . . each qualified health plan shall provide one (or both) . . . a standard package . . . [and a] catastrophic package [both defined]" with covered items and services enumerated.

supplemental benefit package: Any array or set of benefits to be added to the *basic benefit package*. Definition or standardization of the contents of the package is not implied in the term, except in the case of the Medicare supplemental insurance packages; see *Medicare supplement insurance*.

uniform benefit package: See *standard benefit package*.

Uniform Effective Health Benefits (UEHB): A term employed by the *Jackson Hole Group* meaning a "list of effective and appropriate health care services that will constitute the national standard for health care every American will be eligible to receive under the managed competition proposal."

benefits: The money, care, or other services to which an individual is entitled by virtue of insurance. In health care insurance, there are two basic kinds of benefits, indemnity and service (see below).

One serious problem the nation is facing in health care reform is that there is no standard as to the definitions of various benefits from insurer to insurer; a given "benefit statement" by one company may not mean the same as the exact same benefit statement made by another company; that is to say, there are no standard definitions.

indemnity benefits: Insurance benefits provided in cash to the beneficiary rather than in services (*service benefits*). Indemnity benefits are usual with commercial insurance. Sometimes called "indemnity insurance."

portable benefits: An attribute of a health care system in which the beneficiary can move from one employer to another without loss of benefits or having to go through a waiting period. Without portable benefits, individuals often are unwilling to change employment because benefits will be lost. This condition is known as *job lock*.

service benefits: Insurance benefits which are the health care services themselves, rather than money (see *service*). Money benefits are called "*indemnity benefits*." Service benefits are traditional with Blue Cross/Blue Shield (BC/BS) and Medicare.

Benefits Cash Out Commission: Under *HR 1743*, a commission set up to work out the procedures under which an individual could cash out his FEHBP health benefits .

Benefits Commission: Under *HR 3704*, a body of five members appointed by the President, with responsibility for proposing legislation to clarify "covered items and services," specifications on cost-sharing, and provide estimates of cost of the benefit packages. The Commission may not add a new category of benefits.

Benefits, Evaluations, and Data Standards Board (BEDS Board): Under *HR 3222*, a nonprofit corporation under the direction of a board of 5 directors, with duties to: (1) make recommendations to the Health Care Standards Commission (Commission) concerning a) the uniform set of effective benefits, b) the standards for information to be provided by accountable health plans (AHPs), c) auditing standards to ensure the accuracy of such information, and d) aggregate data on coverage decisions made by AHPs and recommendations for evaluations of particular technologies; (2) advise the Commission on evaluations; and (3) assist in the development of standards for the national health data system.

blacklisting: Refusal by insurers to insure high-risk industries, professions, or individuals (especially those who might inherit diseases). If the blacklisting applies to high-risks in a given geographical area, it is called "redlining" (this has been a civil rights issue). Refusal to insure a high-risk industry is also called "industry screening." See *risk (1)*.

Blue Cross (BC): The nonprofit hospital care *prepayment plan* which was developed and sponsored by hospitals, and which originally was restricted to furnishing hospital care. Many BC plans have linked with their counterpart *Blue Shield (BS)* plans, which are physician sponsored, and which deal with physician (medical) care. Some 77 plans of each type, BC and BS, are in existence across the U.S., and state statutes typically govern their operation. While plans are similar in principle, each one is autonomous; there are differences in policies, benefit structure, and administration from plan to plan. When the local BC and BS plans have linked, they are typically referred to jointly as Blue Cross/Blue Shield (BC/BS).

Blue Cross and Blue Shield (BC/BS): The nonprofit health care *prepayment plans* (health insurance plans) which originated with hospitals and physicians, respectively. In many areas the Blue Cross (BC) and Blue Shield (BS) plans have merged. There are about 77 of these health insurance plans linked by a national association, the Blue Cross and Blue Shield Association (BCBSA).

Blue Cross and Blue Shield Association (BCBSA): The national association of the nonprofit health care *prepayment plans*, originated by hospitals and physicians, respectively, called *Blue Cross (BC)* and *Blue Shield (BS)* plans. The original stimulus for the national association was to facilitate the BC and BS plans entering into "national" contracts, for example, with large corporations having plants or offices in the territories of several BC and BS plans, each of which has somewhat different policies and benefit structures.

Blue Indigo: The concept that (1) the health of a population is primarily its own responsibility and (2) health care reform, as well as achievement of improvement of individual health, can only be the result of the mobilization of local resources under community leadership. Innovation and experimentation are fundamental to the concept. The concept originated with a task force of the *National Council of Community Hospitals (NCCH)* and a parallel task force of the faculty of the *Estes Park Institute (EPI)*. A national body, *Indigo Institute*, has been established to undertake further research, develop, and encourage the concept and to assist local communities in its adoption.

Blue Indigo Corporation: A corporation, typically a nonprofit *(501(c)(3))* health-related corporation, which has been formed by a community in order to implement the *Blue Indigo* concept. As the concept develops, a few criteria must be met before a corporation can properly be called a Blue Indigo Corporation: (1) there must be collaborative effort between at least two local organizations, one of them a health care organization; but if there are only two organizations, only one of them should be a health care organization; (2) at least one of the organizations is *not* a governmental unit; (3) primary concern is *health* (rather than simply health *care*)--a Blue Indigo Corporation is not just a new kind of health care delivery system; (4) the organization must serve a defined population; (5) the corporation's efforts may be directed at the solution of any problem which affects the health of the local population, and which the corporation wants to address; (6) goals should be set in such a manner that it is possible to measure their achievement; such measurement is incumbent upon the corporation; (7) physicians and hospitals must participate, but the decision making is in the hands of a governing body which is representative of all the sponsors--i.e., health care providers only provide input along with the other partners in the Blue Indigo process, most importantly, community leaders; (8) only rarely would a state-wide organization qualify for the Blue Indigo Corporation label; the essence of the concept is that the community served be small enough to have common problems and interests.

Blue Shield (BS): The nonprofit medical (physician) care *prepayment plan* which was developed by and sponsored by physicians, and which originally was restricted to furnishing physician care. Many BS plans have linked with their counterpart *Blue Cross (BC)* plans, which are hospital sponsored, and which deal with hospital care. Some 77 plans of each type, BC and BS, are in existence across the U.S., and state statutes typically govern their operation. While plans are similar in principle, each one is autonomous; there are differences in policies, benefit structure, and administration among them from plan to plan. When the local BS and BC plans are linked, they are typically called jointly Blue Cross/Blue Shield (BC/BS).

bond: A written contract which guarantees that something will be done or money will be paid.

performance bond: A bond which guarantees correct and timely performance (for example, construction of a facility) and which will pay money if the performance is not completed.

Breaux bill: See *S 1579.*

BS: See *Blue Shield.*

budget neutrality: A term which came into use as part of the *prospective payment system (PPS)* to mean that the new payment system may not pay hospitals, in the aggregate, any more or less for Medicare patients than the hospitals would have been paid under the previous system. More generally, a budget may be said to be "neutral" if, in total, it is neither larger than nor smaller than the previous budget.

budget reconciliation: A part of the legislative budgeting process which defines federal programs in such a manner that program costs are consistent with Congress' decision as to how much money is to be spent for the program in question.

bundling: Grouping things together into a package. See *unbundling*.

outpatient bundling: A *Health Care Financing Administration (HCFA)* regulation which would require hospitals to "bundle," into the bill to Medicare, diagnostic procedures or tests which are provided to a registered outpatient by outside suppliers, even though the service is provided outside the outpatient department. In the past, such services could be billed separately. The bundling would obtain for services that are the result of an outpatient "*encounter*," i.e., a direct personal contact between a patient and a physician or other person authorized to order services for patient diagnosis or treatment.

C

c(3): See *501(c)(3)*.

c(4): See *501(c)(4)*.

c(6): See *501(c)(6)*.

cafeteria plan: See *Zero Balanced Reimbursement Account (ZEBRA)*.

CAHPIF: See *Corporate Alliance Health Plan Insolvency Fund*.

Canadian-style system: This phrase is often used to describe a single-payer, nationalized or socialized health care system. Actually, Canada has a system consisting of national health insurance and twelve separate single-payer systems--the ten provinces plus two territories--each with a global budget (see *global budgeting*). Most physicians are self-employed and reimbursed under a *negotiated fee schedule*. Patients choose their own physicians. About half of the hospitals are government-owned; the rest are nonprofits which are reimbursed in lump sums. The provinces approve investments in facilities and technologies.
There are five key and indispensable principles of the Canadian system:

universality

comprehensiveness

accessibility

portability

public administration

Proponents of this plan contend that the absence of paperwork (compared with the U.S.) would save enough money to virtually eliminate the cost crisis, that physicians are free from interference in their decisions about patient care, that patients have freedom of choice, and that both physicians and patients like the system.

cap: A limit on the amount of money which may be spent for a given purpose. A global budget for health care for a community would be such a cap; see *global budgeting*.

out-of-pocket cap: A maximum amount which an individual will be required to pay for health care in the form of *copayments* or *deductibles* in a given time period.

capacity limits: Under *HR 3704*, limits which may be granted to a general access plan if it demonstrates to the appropriate certifying authority that its ability to serve already enrolled groups will be impaired if it is required to enroll other *eligible employees* and *eligible individuals*.

capital pass-through: Costs, such as depreciation and interest, which are "passed through." In other words, these costs are not included in the *diagnosis related group (DRG)* prices, but are paid directly to the hospital in the *prospective payment system (PPS)*.

capitation: Capitation is a flat periodic payment to a physician or health care system per person cared-for ("per capita"). The provider assumes the risk that the payment will cover the costs for whatever the patient needs. Careful actuarial study beforehand in determining the amount of the fee makes this far less of a gamble than might be thought. Capitation has probably the lowest administrative cost of any payment mechanism.
Capitation is the most commonly mentioned form of payment in health care reform discussions. Opponents allege that capitation offers too great a temptation to skimp on care in order to enhance profits. Proponents respond that avoiding this problem is one reason to emphasize quality measurements, and adequate supervision of the system.

care: The treatment and other services provided to a patient. Care is often described according to the needs of the patient: for example, neonatal care describes the care given newborns; respiratory care describes the care provided for patients with respiratory (breathing) difficulties. Care may also be described according to the "level" (intensity) or urgency of care, the health professional providing care, or the facility required. See also *level of care*.

care manager: Synonym for "gatekeeper"; short for "patient care manager." See *patient care manager*.

caregiver: Traditionally, an individual who provides care for a disabled or ill friend or relative. The term is now being used for anybody, including physicians, who gives care. A person may also be his or her own caregiver.

carrier: An organization which handles the claims for beneficiaries on behalf of certain kinds of health insurance. A carrier may be an insurance company, a prepayment plan, or a government agency. In general, a carrier is at some risk (see *risk (2)*). On the other hand, an intermediary, which is an agency in the Medicare system which has been selected to pay claims, and which is responsible only for taking care of the administration of the plan, is not at risk.

carving out: A practice by insurers of providing group coverage only to healthy individuals in a small business, while permitting sicker co-workers to purchase only expensive *high risk pool* coverage (see *risk pool*). Carving out is a method of avoiding *adverse selection*. The practice is questionable and sometimes illegal.

case management (1): A traditional term for all the activities which a physician normally performs to insure the coordination of the medical services required by a patient. This is not the same function as that of the "gatekeeper" or "gateway" in *managed care* (see *patient care manager (PCM)*). Under ordinary circumstances, the American Medical Association (AMA) does not consider case management a separately reimbursable service.

case management (2): A term which, when used in connection with *managed care*, covers all the activities of evaluating the patient, planning treatment, referral, and followup, so that care is continuous and comprehensive and payment for the care is obtained. See *patient care manager (PCM)*.

case mix: The mix of cases, defined by age, sex, diagnoses, treatments, *severity of illness*, and so on, handled by a practitioner or hospital. Case mix is defined by: (1) grouping patients (*classification (1)*) according to these factors; and then (2) determining the proportion of the total falling into each group. At present, the most widely used classification for this purpose is the *diagnosis related group (DRG)* system. Sometimes the term "case mix" is used, inaccurately, to mean the grouping system itself (DRG, for example).

   In the Medicare *prospective payment system (PPS)*, which sets a price for each DRG, the total revenue for the hospital for its Medicare patients depends on how many "items" it "sells," and of what kind, that is, the number of patients cared for and the DRG of each. The revenue, therefore, is dependent upon the hospital's case mix.

case mix complexity: A phrase used to convey the idea that hospitals (and physicians) differ in the variety of patients they serve. A specialized hospital would have a less complex mix of patients than a general hospital. The complexity is sometimes described quantitatively by the use of a *case mix index*.

case mix index (CMI): A term used in the *prospective payment system (PPS)*. It is a measure of the "expected costliness," per patient, of treating a given hospital's mix of cases. CMI is scaled so that a hospital whose mix is like that in base data would have a CMI of 1.0. The base data for a CMI usually come from a broad sector of inpatients, often the Medicare patients, discharged from the nation's hospitals during a base year.

For calculating CMIs, a *classification (1)* of patients is used, in which each category (class) is assigned a "weight" that is proportional to the average cost of treating a patient in that class. These weights are calculated from the base data. A hospital's CMI for a given time period may be calculated as follows: (1) for each patient, identify the patient's class and note the associated weight; (2) take the average of these weights.

CMI may also be calculated by the following formula:

$$CMI = \sum_i p_i w_i$$

where i = patient class, p = the proportion of the hospital's patients falling into that class, and w = the weight assigned to that class.

case mix management information system (case mix MIS): See *management information system* under *information system.*

case mix MIS: Case mix management information system. See *management information system* under *information system.*

case mix severity: A term referring, as yet without a single definition, to the degree of illness of a given group of patients. For example, one hospital's (or one time-period's) group of diabetes patients (or a specific *diagnosis related group (DRG)*) may be much more severely ill than another's. Various *"severity of illness"* index methods are under development to quantify this fact.

case mix system: Usually, an *information system* in which clinical and financial data are merged, patient by patient, in such a manner that analyses can be made as to the profitability of a given type of patient (*diagnosis related group (DRG)* category, for example), clinical department, physician, or other aspect of the hospital.

case shifting: See *dumping.*

catastrophic health plan: Under *HR 3080*, " . . . a plan covering specific expenses . . . to the extent such expenses covered by the plan for any calendar year exceed $1,800 ($3,600 if the . . . plan provides coverage for more than 1 individual) or such higher amounts as may be specified by the plan."

catastrophic illness: An illness which requires very costly treatment; one which is catastrophic to the patient's or family's finances. The illness may be either acute or chronic, and it may run its course quickly or over a protracted period.

CBO: See *Congressional Budget Office.*

CBP: Comprehensive benefit package. See *benefit package.*

CCN: See *community care network.*

CCP

CCP: See *community care plan.*

center of care, specialized: See *specialized center of care.*

CER: See *capital expenditure review* under *review.*

certificate of need (CON): A certificate, issued by a governmental or planning agency, which approves the hospital's contention that it needs a given facility or service (for example, open heart surgery). A certificate of need is required under many regulatory situations in order to obtain approval to build, purchase, or institute the service in question.

certificate of public advantage: Under *HR 3080,* a "health care certificate of public advantage" may be issued by the Attorney General in instances in which a health care joint venture is found to qualify, under the Act, for exemption from liability under antitrust laws.

Certified Health Plan: A health plan which has been "certified" by the state in which it is operated or by the *National Health Board* (the Board) proposed in the *Health Security Act (HSA).* This is one type of health plan acceptable under the HSA, the other being a "self-insured" plan, i.e., a group health plan defined as self-insured under the *Employee Retirement Income Security Act (ERISA).*

certifying authority: See *appropriate certifying authority.*

CHA: See *community health authority.*

Chafee bill: See *S 1770.*

chain organization: See *multihospital system.*

CHAMPUS: See *Civilian Health and Medical Program of the Uniformed Services.*

CHAMPVA: See *Civilian Health and Medical Program of the Veterans Administration.*

channeling: A term used in *long-term care* in which efforts are made to avoid institutionalization of patients by having them directed ("channeled") to community-based long-term care services. From 1980 to 1985, the *Health Care Financing Administration (HCFA)* and other federal agencies financed a demonstration of the concept, which used comprehensive *case management (2),* but ended the demonstration when a study showed no lowering of cost. More recently, reports suggest that when a case manager participates in the financial planning as well as the health care decisions, significant savings may be realized.

charge: The dollar amount asked for a *service* by a health care provider. It is contrasted with the *cost,* which is the dollar amount the provider incurs in furnishing the service. It is difficult to determine precise costs for many services, and in such cases charges are substituted for costs in many reimbursement and payment formulas (often with the stipulation that the hospital's bookkeeping follow certain rules).

allowable charge: See *covered charge.*

covered charge: An item of *service* which, when billed to a *third party payer*, will be paid, since it is for a benefit provided under the contract. The charges for television and meals for visitors, for example, are not ordinarily covered charges. Synonym(s): allowable charge.

charitable purpose: Under the *Health Security Act (HSA)*, an organization's provision of health care services would not be considered charitable (for tax exemption purposes) unless the organization, at least annually, and with participation by community representatives, assesses the health care needs of the community, and develops a plan to meet those needs. The provision of health care services by a health maintenance organization (HMO) is not considered a charitable activity (501(c)(3)) unless it meets new requirements proposed as additions to Section 501(m) of the Internal Revenue Code.

charity allowance: A reduction of a *charge* (a discount) to a patient because that patient is *indigent* or *medically indigent*.

CHC: See *Community Health Center*.

cherry picking: A practice by insurers of selling policies only to people who do not need medical care; then dropping them once they do. Synonym(s): cream skimming.

CHIMIS: See *community health integrated management information system* under *information system*.

CHIN: Community health information network. See *community health integrated management information system* under *information system*.

CHIPPA: See *community health planning agency*.

CHN: Community health network. See *community health center*.

CHP: Community health plan; see *Hospital Health Plan*. See also *comprehensive health planning* under *planning*.

CHP agency: See *comprehensive health planning agency*.

chronically ill individual: Under *HR 3080*, "...an individual who is certified by a physician or registered professional nurse as being unable to perform at least 3 activities of daily living (ADL) without substantial assistance from another individual. For purposes of this [definition] the term [ADL] means bathing, dressing, eating, toileting, transferring, and walking."

CHSP: See *Clinton Health Security Plan*.

churning: The practice of *discharge* of a patient from the hospital and *readmission* of the same patient for what is really a single *episode of care* in order to be able to charge for two or more hospitalizations. Only the last discharge is "real" from a medical standpoint--except for the financial benefit of being paid for two or more hospitalizations under the *prospective payment system (PPS)*, there would have been no intermediate discharges.

    price churning: See *predatory pricing*.

churning the books: See *predatory pricing*.

CIHB: See *Commission on Integration of Health Benefits*.

civil monetary penalty: A fine. "Civil" pertains to legal matters which are not criminal, but "penalty" means that the money to be paid is for punishment of the wrongdoer, rather than as compensation to the injured. Synonym: civil money penalty.

The *Health Security Act (HSA)* proposes civil monetary penalties for a number of abuses of the health care system; for example, enticing a Medicare-eligible person to choose a particular provider, improperly limiting health care services, failure to cooperate with a quality assurance or utilization review program, submission of false information to the *National Health Board (NHB)*, a *health alliance*, or specified state and federal agencies.

civil money penalty: See *civil monetary penalty*.

Civilian Health and Medical Program of the Uniformed Services (CHAMPUS): A program that pays for medical care given by civilian providers to retired members of the uniformed services of the U.S., and to the dependents of both active and retired members of these services. The program is administered by the Department of Defense.

Civilian Health and Medical Program of the Veterans Administration (CHAMPVA): The federal program, administered by the Defense Department for the Veterans Administration, which provides care for the dependents of totally-disabled veterans. Care is given by civilian providers.

claim: A request for payment of insurance *benefits* to be paid to or on behalf of a *beneficiary*.

claim form: See *insurance claim form*.

claims filing service: A service offered by private entrepreneurs to Medicare beneficiaries and others with health insurance. The service offers to "file, follow-up, and manage" claims (see *claim*). Often the service charges a "registration" fee plus monthly fees. Such a service, which costs perhaps $100 per beneficiary per year, adds to the cost of health care by that amount and, equally importantly, decreases the individual's benefits by that amount.

claims processing: The procedure by which claims for payment for services are reviewed in order to determine whether they should be paid, and for what amount (see *claim*). The review includes verifying that an authorized provider is submitting the claim, that the person served is a *beneficiary*, that the services are medically reasonable and are for available *benefits*, and the amount to be paid.

class of business: Under *HR 3080*, a group of " . . . small employers with similar demographic characteristics and other similar objective characteristics (not relating to claims experience, health status, industry, occupation, or duration of coverage) . . . for health insurance plans with the same or similar coverage."

classification (1): A scheme for grouping the entities (items) making up a universe into categories. A classification is a systematic scheme of organization of information in which a whole body of things--for example, automobiles, houses, hospitals, or procedures--have been grouped (classified) into categories (classes or "pigeonholes") so that the groups can be compared, studied, analyzed, or otherwise processed. Classifications are used in health care to organize patient (and patient care) information for such purposes as studying diseases, assessing quality of care, and determining charges to be made for health care services. Confusion results when the word classification (the whole schema) is used when "class" is intended.

The purpose of the classification determines its organization or grouping system. A classification to describe the body of hospitalized patients requires different groupings than one for general office practice. For example, patients with the common cold are so rarely hospitalized that, in a hospital diagnosis classification, the common cold is grouped with miscellaneous respiratory conditions, while in general office practice the common cold may be seen so frequently that it deserves a category of its own.

classification (2): Derived from the verb "to classify." The process of placing an entity (item) of a universe into its category (pigeonhole) within a *classification (1)*. This is a specialized function which requires a "judgment call" as to which category a given entity falls into in cases where the entity is described in a term or terms which are not found in the classification as printed (or its index). Classification requires expert knowledge of the universe of objects to be classified, in contrast to "coding," which is a clerical task. See *coding*.

clear and convincing evidence: Under *HR 3080*, "... that measure or degree of proof that will produce in the mind of the trier of fact a firm belief or conviction as to the truth of the allegations sought to be established, except that such measure or degree of proof is more than that required under preponderance of the evidence, but less than that required for proof beyond a reasonable doubt."

clearinghouse: See *health care information clearinghouse*.

CLICKS: See *Clinical Information System* under *information system*.

clinical care path: See *critical path*.

clinical nurse midwife (CNM): A nurse midwife.@TERM = Clinical Practice Guidelines (CPGs): See *guidelines (2)*.

Clinton Health Security Plan (CHSP): The plan now embodied in the *Health Security Act (HSA)*.

"Clinton Lite": Media reference to *HR 3222*.

CMHC: Community mental health center. See *community mental health service program*.

CMI: See *case mix index*.

CMP: See *competitive medical plan*.

CNM: See *clinical nurse midwife..*

COB: See *coordination of benefits.*

COBRA: See *Consolidated Omnibus Budget Reconciliation Act.*

code: A unique symbol (usually alphanumeric) having a one-to-one correspondence with a term or a rubric. Codes may be used on the patient's bill, for example, to indicate the *service* for which the charge is shown. Diagnoses and procedures are commonly coded for ease of manipulation by computer (see *coding*).

code sets: Under *HR 3704*, " . . . any codes used for supplying specific data in a uniform data set, including tables of terms, medical diagnostic codes, medical procedure codes, identification numbers, and any code sets of the National Uniform Billing Committee, the Health Care Financing Administration, or the American National Standards Institute (ANSI).

coding: The process of substituting a symbol (*code*), usually a number, for a term, such as a diagnosis or procedure. Coding ordinarily has three purposes: (1) to compress the information from a string of letters or words into a compact, usually uniform, space; (2) to facilitate handling the information by mechanical (computer) methods; and (3) to introduce precision (reduce ambiguity), since numbers are not subject to spelling errors and it is easier to make an exact check of a number than of a word. (Inventories are controlled, for example, by code numbers rather than narrative descriptions of their contents.)

Coding is a clerical function and should only require substituting a code for the term to be coded. However, in many circumstances, the term to be coded will not be found in the coder's reference material, and a judgment will have to be made. In this case, the coder must know both the meaning of the term and also the way the coding system works, so that proper coding can be done. Under such circumstances, the task is far from clerical, and is really one of *classification (2)* rather than coding.

There are two basic ways to code: (1) assigning to each individual entity (term) its own unique code (number); and (2) assigning to each term a code which represents a category, which category may include one or more individual entities (terms). The first technique is called "*entity coding*"; the second is "*category coding.*" These are discussed further:

category coding: Coding in which each code (number) represents (the rubric of) a category rather than an individual term being coded. Category coding is designed to achieve grouping to established classification "pigeonholes" in a single step which combines coding and classifying.

Category coding is the method presently used by hospitals for coding diagnoses and procedures. This coding is done for the indexing of medical records for retrieval and research, and in the submission of discharge abstracts for billing. Each diagnosis and procedure is given the code for the category of diagnoses or procedures to which it belongs, rather than a unique code ("entity code") which represents the diagnosis or procedure itself.

Except for "single-diagnosis categories," the (diagnosis of the) case cannot be retrieved precisely because decoding retrieves the rubric (label) of the category rather than the specific diagnosis or procedure which was coded. For example, a specific new condition such as AIDS (acquired immune deficiency syndrome), which had not been foreseen and had no category or pigeonhole of its own, for several years was placed into various categories, such as the "waste basket" category labelled "other immune deficiency disorders." Such a system makes it impossible, without going back to the original medical records, to determine the exact number of AIDS cases or to retrieve them by themselves; all cases of "other immune deficiency disorders" are counted and retrieved together.

In the coding system now in use in the U.S., which is a category coding system (*ICD-9-CM*), over 100,000 diagnostic terms are forced into 11,000 groups or classes; further detail is lost when these categories, in turn, go into the 468 DRGs (see *diagnosis related group (DRG)*). It is worth noting that this system violates a basic purpose of coding, the achievement of precise information.

entity coding: Coding in which each code represents an individual "entity" (term) rather than a category (group) of terms. In entity coding, each entity (specific term) to be coded (for example, a diagnosis or procedure) is exchanged for a code (number) which, when decoded, yields exactly the same words (term) which were coded. No detail is lost as is the case in *category coding*; entity coding achieves one of the major purposes of coding, the elimination of ambiguity in the information in order to increase its precision, since numbers are not subject to spelling errors and it is easier to make an exact check of a number than of a word.

The principle behind entity coding is that *classification (2)* should be a two-step process: in the first step, information is coded so that it can be manipulated (usually by a computer); and, in the second step, the coded information is then classified according to the needs of the particular user or the demands of a particular *classification (1)* system. In entity coding, the integrity of the items of information remains intact, and the system can meet the needs of any number of classification systems. For example, a person investigating the frequency of office visits for various medical problems would need to have a discrete class for the common cold because of its frequency in that setting. Since common colds seldom require hospitalization, however, placing the cold in a category of "other respiratory diseases" or "other infectious diseases" might meet the needs of the hospital studying reasons for admission.

cognitive services: See *service*.

coinsurance: A type of insurance which requires that a percentage of the charges be paid by the *beneficiary*, the primary purpose being to discourage small claims and "over-use" of services. Usually there is also a *deductible* which the beneficiary pays before the coinsurance begins. For example, the insured may pay the first $500 per year under the deductible; after charges exceed $500, the insurer would pay 80% of all charges over $500, and the beneficiary would pay the remaining 20%. Most policies today limit the out-of-pocket expense of the beneficiary to a ceiling; for example, $5,000. See also *copayment*.

collaborative care: See *managed care.*

comfort care: Medical or other health care whose sole or primary purpose is the comfort of the patient. In the *Oregon plan*, comfort care is defined to include health services which are diagnostic, curative, or focused on active treatment of the primary condition and intended to prolong life. Examples of comfort care include pain medication, hospice services, medical equipment and supplies (beds, wheelchairs, etc.), palliative services for symptom relief (e.g. radiation therapy). See also *hospice program*.:

Commission on Integration of Health Benefits (CIHB): Under the *Health Security Act (HSA)*, a 15-member body to be appointed by the Secretary of Health and Human Services (HHS) and the Secretary of Labor jointly, with the assignment to study the feasibility and appropriateness of transferring financial responsibility for all medical benefits (including those currently covered under workers compensation and automobile insurance) to health plans.

Commission on Professional and Hospital Activities (CPHA): An independent nonprofit organization based in Ann Arbor, Michigan, dedicated to the improvement of health care quality through the use of comparative data. It was formed in 1955 with the national sponsorship of the American College of Physicians (ACP), the American College of Surgeons (ACS), and the American Hospital Association (AHA). CPHA provides certain shared clinical and management information services (MIS) data processing, performs interpretive research services for hospitals and other health care institutions, and disseminates information to the health care field. Its largest and oldest program is the prototype hospital discharge abstract system, the Professional Activity Study (PAS). CPHA, 1105 Eisenhower Place, P.O. Box 304, Ann Arbor, MI 48106-0304. Telephone 313-995-9800.

Communitarian Network: A Washington DC-based group which advocates shared responsibility and community-based decision making. A recent paper, "Core Values in Health Care Reform," proposes that it is important that health care reforms not undermine the culture of care in their pursuit of savings and improvement of access.

community care network (CCN): The focal point of the American Hospital Association's plan for health care reform. The network would consist of local groups of physicians and clinics, organized by hospitals, competing for contracts with group insurers to provide care to enrolled individuals. The payment schedule would be established by an independent regulatory board, and providers would normally be reimbursed on a capitated basis.

community care plan (CCP): The *Eutaw Group's* alternative to (or complement to) the *accountable health plan (AHP)* in the health care reform movement (1993). A CCP is expected to carry out a proactive "predict and manage" philosophy; its proponents see the AHP as essentially a "treat and/or prevent what comes in the door" organization. It is directed at "equal health status" rather than "equity in prices per capita," as it describes the AHP's goal. A CCP would offer (1) "essential gateway services," accessible via a "gateway" in the hands of a generalist (physician or allied health professional, with physician oversight; see *patient care manager (PCM))* and (2) "essential referral services."

The gateway services would consist of "assessment of health needs via surveillance, outreach, and screening, using traditional public health approaches and nontraditional proactive health (home and school) visitors; entry to care networks; child and adult therapeutic and preventive generalist care; emergency services; AIDS counseling; sexually transmitted disease (STD) intervention; family planning; maternity care; nutrition services; mental health services; dental services; social support; transportation; and home health. The referral services would include hospital care ranging from full service down to "essential access" community hospitals, hospice, nursing home, and rehabilitation. The West Alabama Health Services project in Eutaw County, Alabama, is a prototype program of the Eutaw Group.

community case manager: Under *HR 3704*, "... an individual or entity which i) has experience or has been trained in providing case management services and in preparing individual care plans; ii) has experience in assessing individuals to determine their functional and cognitive impairment; iii) is not a relative of the individual receiving case management services . . . " If such an individual meets requirements prescribed by the Secretary [of Health and Human Services], the person may be classed as a "qualified community case manager."

community health authority (CHA): Under *HR 3573*, an entity proposed as a means of "providing access to cost-effective preventive and primary care and related services for various areas and populations, including low-income residents of medically underserved areas or for medically underserved populations."

community health center (CHC): A term used loosely to cover community, migrant, and homeless health centers. Over 30 years ago, the federal government established a network of community and migrant health centers through grants from the U.S. Public Health Service. There are now 571 of these centers. Two-thirds of their patients are women and children. The centers employ or contract for the services of 3,600 physicians as well as other providers. To these centers have been added 119 homeless health centers through the Health Care for the Homeless Programs, also with funds from the U.S. Public Health Service. The total is 690 centers. All together, they provide comprehensive preventive and primary health services to *medically underserved populations*, both rural and urban, of more than 7,000,000 people at 1,400 sites across the country, including Puerto Rico and the District of Columbia. The centers are built on a public-private partnership and are supported by federal, state, and local funds, as well as by private sources. The term includes "neighborhood health centers," "family health centers," and "community health networks (CHNs)." Sometimes called a "Section 330" [of the Public Health Service Act] health services group.

Further information can be obtained from the National Association of Community Health Centers, Inc., 1330 New Hampshire Ave. NW, Washington, DC 20036. Telephone 202-659-8008.

Community Health Improvement Act of 1993:   See *HR 3573*.

community health information network (CHIN):   See *community health integrated management information system (CHIMIS)* under *information system*.

community health integrated management information system (CHIMIS) :   See *information system*.

community health network (CHN):   See *community health center*.

community health plan (CHP):   See *Hospital Health Plan (HHP)*.

community health planning agency (CHIPPA):   The term employed in Florida for the organizations established by statute in 1993 to serve the same function as *health alliances* (HAs). The state is to be covered by 11 of these agencies.

community health services: A term which encompasses preventive procedures, diagnosis, and treatment for residents of a community. It does not imply any organizational structure.

community mental health center (CMHC):   See *community mental health service program*.

community mental health service program: An organization set up to provide mental health services to a defined community. Synonym(s): community mental health center (CMHC).

community rating: See *rating*.

community resource management (CRM):   The concept, in health care, that the unit which should be considered in the allocation of resources is the entire community rather than each of its component organizations.

comparative value information: Under *HR 3080*, " . . . at least the average prices of common health care services [defined as 'such procedures as the Secretary may specify' and any additional services which a State may wish to include] . . . and measures of variability."

compensation: In addition to the common meaning of payment for work done, compensation covers systems to make reparation for damage or injury done. Traditionally, patients who have been injured by the health care system, either by *malpractice* or otherwise, have sought compensation by filing a claim--which usually results in a lawsuit--against the health care provider. This system is lengthy and costly, and does not always provide a fair result. Thus, alternatives such as *patients' compensation* (see below) have been proposed.

neo-no-fault compensation: See *patients' compensation*.

no-fault compensation: A system of compensation for persons who have been injured or adversely affected, without the need to prove fault or wrongdoing. No-fault systems are presently in use to compensate auto and industrial accident victims (see *workers' compensation*). Several no-fault (or no-fault-like) plans have been suggested for the health care area; see, for example, *patients' compensation*.

patients' compensation: A *no-fault* system for compensating patients who suffer harm as a result of some aspect of medical or hospital care, proposed as an alternative to *malpractice* litigation. Some of the principles behind *workers' compensation* have been applied in the patients' compensation proposal. Synonym(s): neo-no-fault compensation.

workers' compensation (WC): A system of compensating workers for on-the-job injuries, developed as an alternative to lawsuits by injured employees. The typical workers' compensation law compensates workers who suffer work-related injuries (regardless of fault), and provides that workers' compensation benefits are the "exclusive remedy," the only means of receiving compensation for work-related injuries and illnesses. Workers may therefore not sue their employers. Workers' compensation was formerly called workmen's compensation.

In some states, workers' compensation also covers injuries or illnesses resulting from negligent treatment (by the employer) of work-related injuries or illness; in that case, workers' compensation is usually the exclusive remedy for the negligent treatment, and the worker-patient cannot sue the employer for *malpractice.*

Under the *Health Security Act (HSA)* the costs of workers' compensation would be "folded in" to health care costs as a method of cost containment.

compensation fund: See *alternative dispute resolution.*

competitive medical plan (CMP): A health care plan which has met requirements of the federal government and thus become qualified to accept Medicare *vouchers* from Medicare beneficiaries, and which in turn provides the beneficiaries with all Medicare services. The Medicare vouchers are negotiable only with competitive medical plans which have met the eligibility requirements.

Complaint Review Office (CRO): Under the *Health Security Act (HSA),* an office established by states, in accordance with rules established by the Secretary of Labor, whose purpose it would be to review complaints as to denial of payment for services. Such an office would be established for each regional health alliance, and would hear complaints for corporate health alliances as well. See *health alliance.*

comprehensive benefit package (CBP): See *benefit package.*

comprehensive health care: Services that are intended to meet all the health care needs of a patient: outpatient, inpatient, home care, and other.

comprehensive health care delivery system: A health care delivery system which includes both facilities and professionals, and which is set up to provide *comprehensive health care* to a defined population.

comprehensive health planning agency (CHP agency): An *agency* established in response to a federal health planning act in 1966, which was later replaced by a group of agencies established under federal legislation passed in 1974. The latter agencies were the health systems agencies (HSAs), state health planning and development agencies, and statewide health coordinating councils (SHCCs).

computer-based patient record (CPR): A medical record still under development by a number of individuals and organizations. It was given new impetus by a report from the Institute of Medicine (IOM) in 1991, and the *Computer-Based Patient Record Institute (CPRI)* was formed to pursue and coordinate the efforts.

Computer-Based Patient Record Institute (CPRI): An organization formed in 1991 to establish routine use of a *computer-based patient record (CPR)* system in all health care settings. Its formation was recommended in a study by the Institute of Medicine (IOM), *The Computer-Based Patient Record*, which was published earlier in 1991. The study called for fully-automated medical records in hospitals by the end of the decade. Advocates content that such a record would radically change health care delivery by improving efficiency, quality of care, and cost containment. CPRI was formed by a coalition of about 35 interested groups, which included the American Medical Association (AMA), the American Health Information Management Association (AHIMA), and the US Chamber of Commerce. Membership is for corporations only (there are in 1993 twenty-five corporate members); there are no individual memberships, although individuals may obtain the newsletter and participate in certain activities and work groups. CPRI, 919 N. Michigan Avenue, Chicago IL 90911. Telephone 800-382-2973.

Computerized Patient Information System (CPIS): See *information system*.

CON: See *certificate of need*.

Congressional Budget Office (CBO): An organization, created by the Congressional Budget Act of 1974, which provides the U.S. Congress with analyses of alternative fiscal, programmatic, and budgetary issues. It has been involved in studying and making recommendations concerning the costs of alternative health care reform proposals.

Congressional Research Service (CRS): A part of the Library of Congress which performs studies for Congress.

consistent with practice guidelines: Under *HR 3222*, refers to practice guidelines established by the *Agency for Clinical Evaluations* (Agency) established under this Act. (See *guidelines (2)*.)

Consolidated Omnibus Budget Reconciliation Act of 1985 (COBRA): A federal law with at least two important provisions for health care. One requires that employers of 20 or more workers must continue former employees' health insurance coverage (at the former employee's expense) for up to three years for qualified beneficiaries. The law amends the Internal Revenue Code of 1954.

Under the *Health Security Act (HSA)*, this requirement would be amended so that the employer would be relieved of this responsibility as soon as the individual became eligible for comprehensive coverage under HSA.

Another important section of the Act is the "Emergency Medical Treatment and Active Labor Act" (42 U.S.C. 1395(d)), which prohibits hospitals from discharging or transferring, for financial reasons, a patient in an "emergency medical condition." This is known as an "anti-dumping" law (see *dumping*).

consumer: An individual who does or may receive health care services. In the context of health care programs or legislation, a consumer is not a *provider*. See also *customer*.

consumer choice (1): A reform approach which would get individuals to purchase health insurance by making it mandatory but providing a tax break; the poor would get a tax refund. Companies providing insurance would not get a tax break. Also called the "market-based approach."

consumer choice (2): Under the *Health Security Act (HSA)*, permission for the individual to obtain (or the employer to provide) coverage in addition to the comprehensive benefit package. The coverage could be obtained by direct purchase or through supplementary insurance.

Consumer Choice Health Security Act of 1993: See *S 1743*.

consumer report card: See *report card*.

continuity of care: The degree to which the care of a patient from the onset of illness until its completion is continuous, that is, without interruption. Interruptions occur sometimes because the patient does not follow through, sometimes because the system has gaps, often because of lack of facilities or because of financial impediments (absence of *benefits*, for example, which cover certain services). The term should be used with a modifier, e.g. "excellent continuity of care."
   The term "continuity of care" is sometimes used to refer to a longer span of time than the single episode of illness, and to the patient's health care when he is both well and ill.

contract provider organization (CPO): See *preferred provider organization*.

conversion: Retaining health insurance when changing employers without having to be reevaluated as to insurability. An employee retiring or otherwise ineligible to remain in a group usually converts to an individual health insurance policy. The privilege to convert in this manner is guaranteed in many circumstances by the *Consolidated Omnibus Budget Reconciliation Act of 1985 (COBRA)*.

conversion factor: A dollar amount for one base unit in the *relative value scale (RVS)*. The price to be paid to the provider for a given service equals the relative value of the service multiplied by the dollar amount of the conversion factor. For example, a blood sugar determination might have a relative value of 5.0, and the conversion factor might be $5.00. The "price" of the blood sugar determination would therefore be $25.00.

converter: Federal terminology for the *conversion factor* used in the *prospective payment system (PPS)*.

Cooper-Grandy bill: See *HR 3222*.

coordinated care: See *managed care*.

coordination of benefits (COB): An insurance claims review process used when a beneficiary is insured by two or more carriers (see *claim*). The process determines the liability of each carrier in order to eliminate duplication of payments. For example, benefits to which an individual is entitled under *workers' compensation* (see *compensation*) are not permitted to be duplicated by ordinary health insurance, even though the injury or illness would be covered were the problem not work-related.

copayment: A fixed sum which a *beneficiary* pays for health services, regardless of the actual charge, and the insurer pays the remainder. For example, the beneficiary may pay $10 for each office visit, $75 for each day in the hospital, and $5 for each drug prescription. See also *coinsurance*.

corporate alliance: See *corporate health alliance* under *health alliance*.

Corporate Alliance Health Plan Insolvency Fund (CAHPIF): A fund to be established and administered by the Secretary of Labor under the *Health Security Act (HSA)*.

corporate health alliance: See *health alliance*.

corporate liability: See *liability (1)*.

Corps, The: See *National Health Service Corps*.

cosmetic surgery: Under *HR 1743*, " . . . any procedure which is directed at improving the patient's appearance and does not meaningfully promote the proper function of the body or prevent or treat illness or disease."

cost: The expense incurred in providing a product or service. A number of modifiers are used with "cost":

allowable cost: Items of *service* which are contractually included in the *benefits* of an insurance or payment plan, similar to "*covered charges*" (see *charge)*. The charges for television and meals for visitors are not ordinarily allowable costs.

capital cost: The cost of developing or acquiring new equipment, facilities, or services; that is, the investment cost to the institution of such growth.

direct cost: A cost which can be identified directly with any part of the hospital organization which the hospital designates as a "cost center." In fact, cost centers are defined as such because they are segments of the hospital, such as the operating rooms, to which direct costs can be assigned rather clearly. To the direct costs of each cost center are added, on the basis of some accounting formula, allocated proportions of the hospital's *indirect costs* (costs, such as for heat and housekeeping, which are not easily allocated to specific cost centers).

fixed cost: A cost which is entirely independent of the volume of activity. If no charges are made for individual local calls, the cost of local telephone service is a fixed cost; on the other hand, long distance service, which depends as it does on the number and length of calls made, is a *variable cost* (however, an unlimited WATS line would be a fixed cost).

indirect cost: There are two kinds of indirect costs in a hospital. The first kind is costs which must be incurred by any organization furnishing services, but which cannot be exactly identified with any specific service rendered or support department. For example, the cost of having a chief executive officer (CEO) is necessary, but it cannot be charged directly to, for example, the operating room as can the salaries of operating room nurses. The second kind of indirect costs is the costs of "support activities," the costs of which can be determined, but which do not produce revenue. Such activities (for example, a hospital's medical record department) have clear direct costs, and must bear their share of the indirect costs of the first type above. But, since these activities do not produce revenue, their costs--both direct and indirect--become indirect costs for the revenue-producing departments and services.

marginal cost: The addition to total cost resulting from the production of an additional unit of service or product. This cost varies with the volume of the operation. A hospital, for example, has a high cost for its first meal served. Subsequent meals have much lower costs each (marginal costs) until the volume is so large as to require changes in facilities, supervision, and the like. At this point the marginal cost will usually rise until a new equilibrium ("optimum output level") is established.

pass-through cost: A term with a specific definition in the *prospective payment system (PPS)*. It refers to hospital costs, such as for medical education, which are not incorporated in the *diagnosis related group (DRG)* prices. Funds are provided to the hospital directly, that is, outside the per-case payments for patient care; the costs are simply passed through (or outside of) the DRG mechanism.

reasonable cost: A term with a specific definition given by the federal government for use in Medicare. It is used only in connection with services in institutions which are exempt from the *prospective payment system (PPS)* and for beneficiaries who are not inpatients.

semi-variable cost: A cost which is partly a *variable cost* and partly a *fixed cost* in its behavior in response to changes in volume. Automobile rental is typically a semi-variable cost, with a fixed charge per day and a variable charge depending on miles driven.

variable cost: A cost which is entirely dependent on the volume of activity, as opposed to a *fixed cost*, which is not affected by volume. In a typical telephone billing system, for example, long distance calls represent a variable cost while local calls represent a fixed cost.

cost allocation: An accounting procedure by which costs that cannot be clearly identified with any specific *cost center* are distributed among cost centers, and by which the costs of support services are distributed among revenue-producing services so as to be recovered in the charges.

cost-benefit analysis: A technique for placing a numerical value on the benefits to be derived from using a piece of equipment or operating a program as compared with its costs. See *cost-benefit ratio*.

cost-benefit ratio: A mathematical expression of the benefits of a given service or the use of certain equipment compared with its costs. To develop such a ratio, both costs and benefits must be expressed in dollars, a task much easier for costs than benefits in many health care situations (improved *quality of life* may truly be a benefit, but expressing it in dollars is, at best, difficult). A ratio of 1.0 means that the benefits and costs are equal; a ratio over 1.0 means that the benefits exceed the costs; and a ratio under 1.0 means that the costs exceed the benefits.

cost center: An area of activity of the hospital with which *direct costs* can be identified. Accounting practice is to assign direct costs to such cost centers, and to allocate to each cost center its proportionate share of *indirect costs*, in order to give management a tool for cost control (or pricing). When a cost center is also revenue-producing, that is, an area for which charges are made (for example, an operating room), the allocation of direct and indirect costs, along with data about the services rendered, permits the charge for each service to be sufficient to cover the cost of that service.

Some other cost centers, over which management wants to maintain control, do not produce revenue. An example is the medical record department. The costs of such departments (direct plus indirect costs) are reallocated as indirect costs to the revenue-producing cost centers.

cost containment: Efforts to prevent increase in cost or to restrict its rate of increase. Cost containment is rarely addressed at reducing cost.

cost control: A term usually applied to an external constraint of costs (or charges), such as legislation or the actions of a regulatory agency.

cost-effective: Providing a service at a "reasonable" cost (which might not necessarily be the lowest cost).

cost-effectiveness analysis: The comparison of the *cost-benefit ratio*s for the same service provided by different methods or with different equipment.

cost-per-case management: The method (philosophy) of hospital management in which hospitals try to control the costs for each kind of case so that the revenue for that case will cover the cost. Cost-per-case management is a new style of management which was developed when hospital revenue changed from reimbursement for services rendered to prospectively determined prices for various kinds of services. This change in reimbursement, in turn, came from the adoption of the *prospective payment system (PPS)* in the Medicare program. Previously, hospitals simply had to ensure that the aggregate of income covered the aggregate of costs.

Cost Quality Management System (CQMS): A system which merges clinical and financial data, patient-by-patient, in a hospital. The diagnosis and procedure data are standardized by use of the *International Classification of Diseases, 9th Revision, Clinical Modification (ICD-9-CM)*, while the financial data are standardized by use of the *International Classification of Clinical Services (ICCS)*. The system is intended to facilitate data display for the individual hospital and also to permit valid comparisons among institutions and services through reference to the data base maintained by the

Commission on Professional and Hospital Activities (CPHA). CQMS is a joint venture between CPHA and Arthur Andersen & Company.

cost-sharing: Out-of-pocket payment by patients for part of the cost of benefits of an insurance plan. The term is not properly applied to sharing in the cost of the insurance premium; it applies only to *deductibles, coinsurance,* and *copayments*.

Under the *Health Security Act (HSA)*, three options are proposed: (1) lower cost sharing, in which the amount the enrollee pays is less; (2) higher cost sharing, in which the amount the enrollee pays is higher; and (3) combination, which, in general involves low cost sharing if the enrollee uses in-network providers and high cost sharing for use of out-of-network items and services. Further provision is made for reduced cost sharing for low income individuals.

cost sharing plan: Under the *Health Security Act (HSA)*, a health insurance policy (or plan) which offers alliance-eligible individuals coverage for deductibles, coinsurance, and copayments required by the *comprehensive benefit package (CBP)* (see *benefit package*).

cost-shifting: Increasing the charges to one group of patients when the payment for another group of patients will not cover the costs for that group. When the government pays too little for its beneficiaries, for example, through the prospective payment system (PPS), it is clear that the cost will be shifted to other payers. Originally, cost-shifting passed the cost on to private-pay patients. As that number of patients has declined, the shift has been from government payers to insurance, most of which is still paid by employers. The resulting disproportionate escalation in insurance premiums has had two significant effects: (1) self-insurance by many more employers, rather than the purchase of health insurance, and (2) increasing interest on the part of employers in health care reform.

cost-to-charge ratio: A term used in finance, which shows whether a *charge* for a given product or service is set so that it covers the *cost*. A ratio of 1.0 means that the cost and charge are identical; a ratio greater than 1.0 means that the charge does not recover the cost; and a ratio less than 1.0 means that the charge exceeds the cost. See also *ratio of costs to charges*.

coverage: In health care reform discussions, "coverage" is most often used to describe the group of people for whom health insurance is available, rather than the particular services paid for (see *benefits* and *insurance coverage*). For example, coverage may be for senior citizens (as a part of Medicare), for those persons who opt to purchase Medicare supplement insurance, for employees of a given company, and so on. In the health care reform movement, "universal coverage" is a goal:

universal coverage: Generally understood to mean coverage for all persons, rather than for some subset of the population. It is often said that "universal coverage is based on citizenship rather than employment," but this raises a question of whether aliens (legal and illegal) would be covered, and under what circumstances. Some writings about the proposed reform measures avoid this issue by referring to "Americans."

Under the *Health Security Act (HSA)*, universal coverage would mean that every United States citizen, resident alien, and long-term nonimmigrant would be covered by health insurance, i.e., the comprehensive benefit package established under the bill. Medicare eligible individuals would, in general, remain under Medicare, and prisoners, military personnel, and Veterans Affairs and Indian Health Service beneficiaries would receive care from the current sources.

Under the *Health Equity and Access Reform Today Act of 1993 (HEART)* *(HR 3704)*, universal coverage is for "each individual who is a citizen or lawful permanent resident . . ." (Non-legal residents will, of course, still require care).

covered home infusion drug: Under the *Health Security Act (HSA)*, a drug which meets certain criteria in HSA as to safety and effectiveness when administered in the home, using a device which is inserted through the skin and also a device to control the rate of flow of the drug.

covered items and services: Under *HR 3704*, " . . . only when the provision of the item or service is medically necessary or appropriate: 1) medical and surgical services (and supplies incident to such services; 2) medical equipment; 3) prescription drugs and biologicals; 4) preventive services; 5) rehabilitation and home services related to an acute care episode; 6) services for severe mental illness; 7) substance abuse services; 8) hospice services; and 9) emergency transportation and transportation for non-elective medically necessary services in frontier and similar areas."

CPGs: Clinical Practice Guidelines. See *guidelines (2).*

CPHA: See *Commission on Professional and Hospital Activities (CPHA).*

CPIS: See *Computerized Patient Information System* under *information system.*

CPM: Critical Path Method. See *critical path.*

CPO: Contract provider organization. See *preferred provider organization.*

CPR: See *computer-based patient record* and *customary, prevailing, reasonable charge.* (Also is an abbreviation for cardio-pulmonary rescusitation.)

CPT: *Current Procedural Terminology.* See *Physicians' Current Procedural Terminology.*

CQI: See *continuous quality improvement* under *quality improvement.*

CQMS: See *Cost Quality Management System.*

cream skimming: See *cherry picking.*

credentialing: A term used to describe the process of determining eligibility for hospital medical staff membership, and privileges to be granted, to physicians and other health care professionals in the light of their academic preparation, licensing, training, and performance. "Privileges" are rights granted by the governing body of the hospital to members of the medical staff, giving them permission to carry out specified diagnostic and therapeutic procedures within the hospital and, in some cases, to admit patients.

Credentials and performance are periodically reviewed, and medical staff membership (and/or privileges) may be denied, modified, or withdrawn.

economic credentialing: Taking a physician's or other professional's "economic behavior" into account in deciding upon medical staff appointment (or reappointment). Hospitals, in an attempt to control hospital costs, have increasingly tried to exclude from their medical staffs physicians whose patients' bills are extraordinarily high when compared to the same kinds of patients of other physicians. A recent Florida circuit court case, *Rosenblum v. Tallahassee Memorial Regional Medical Center*, ruled that a hospital board has a fiduciary duty to protect the assets of the hospital, and thus was justified in taking only financial factors into account in its decision.

critical path: A statement of what steps and procedures should be carried out for the diagnostic evaluation of a patient or for the management (treatment) for a given diagnosis or problem, and the optimum sequence with which they should be carried out. The term comes from the Critical Path Method (CPM), which is similar to the *Program Evaluation and Review Technique (PERT)*, first described in connection with project management procedures developed during World War II. CPM is called a project network technique, it is typically developed with the aid of a computer, and is graphically displayed as a sort of road map.

A major influence toward the use of CPM in medical care was the emergence of teams for taking care of patients, and the communication problems which ensued (there was less need for coordination when medical care involved only the one physician). The goal of critical paths is to insure that (only) the indicated steps are taken, that they are taken in the correct sequence, and distributed over the shortest time consonant with high quality of care. As a result, the quality of care should be optimal and the cost minimal. Because resources vary from hospital to hospital, critical paths are usually produced locally, in contrast with *guidelines (2)*, which generally come from authoritative bodies. Also called clinical care paths.

Critical Path Method (CPM): See *critical path*.

CRM: See *community resource management*.

CRO: See *complaint review office*.

cross-functional: A term used in *quality management* teams to indicate that more than one department is involved. For example, if both nursing and pharmacy are involved in a team, the team is a cross-functional team.

CRS: See *Congressional Research Service*.

custodial care: See *rest home care*.

customary fee: See *customary, prevailing, reasonable charge (or fee) (CPR)*.

customary, prevailing, reasonable charge (or fee) (CPR): The *charge* or "fee" (same as charge), usually of a physician, which has traditionally been defined as that charge which is the lowest of the following: the actual charge made for the *service*; the physician or supplier's "customary" (usual) charge for the service; or the fee "prevailing" in the community for the service. Such fees vary according to specialty, geographic area, and the physician's charge system. Increases in such fees are typically limited by economic indexes imposed by the paying agency. The definition of "reasonable and customary charge (or fee)" is under scrutiny by the federal government with the idea that the fees should be "inherently" reasonable, that is, related to some real worth of the service rather than a comparison. The *Tax Equity and Fiscal Responsibility Act (TEFRA)* and Medicare *regulations* both give specific formulas for calculating the "reasonable charges" limitation on physician fees. Synonym(s): customary fee, prevailing fee.

customer: In health care, "customer" is often used to mean the person or entity buying the services. For example, an employer might be the customer of a *health care plan* which enrolls the employees. See also *consumer*.

In the context of quality management, the customer is the person (or department) for whom services are provided. For example, the customers of the clinical laboratory include not only the patient, but the physician who receives the lab results, and perhaps the accounting department which must determine the charges. An important process in *quality improvement* is to determine who the customers are, what they need, and whether these needs are being met.

cybernaught: A "traveller" in *cyberspace*.

cyberspace: Computer-generated space, in which the traveller is called a "cybernaught." The term was coined by science fiction author William Gibson in 1984. It is now also being applied to computer conferencing, computer bulletin boards, and other innovative communication activities and applications of information technology, particularly in education and health care. An example: a college course is sometimes said to be conducted in cyberspace when it is carried out primarily or largely with an electronic network rather than in a classroom. Students in such a course may be employed in widely separated sites, and the faculty member may address them informally in the electronic network from wherever she happens to be. The reference library is, of course, electronic. Questions, answers, and student and faculty discussion may be posted on the class's computer bulletin board at any time by students or faculty. In addition, scheduled interactive "class periods" for the dispersed faculty and students are held.

D

---

damages: A legal term describing the money to be paid to a *plaintiff* by the *defendant* when the defendant is found to be liable (see *liability (1)*). Only certain kinds of damages, some of which are described below, are permitted. The term "damages" is sometimes used more restrictively to describe the monetary value of the plaintiff's injuries, property loss, and the like.

actual damages: Money paid to compensate actual loss by the plaintiff, such as medical expenses, loss of earnings (or value of services, such as homemaking), *pain and suffering*, and (rarely) *emotional distress.* Synonym(s): compensatory damages.

compensatory damages: See *actual damages.*

economic damages: Under *HR 3080*, " . . . damages paid to compensate an individual for hospital or other medical expense, lost wages, lost employment, and other pecuniary losses."

exemplary damages: See *punitive damages.*

liquidated damages: An amount of money decided on by the parties to a contract at the time of contracting, which will be paid to one party upon default of the other. Such damages are permitted only if the actual amount of damages is very difficult to ascertain, and if the amount is reasonable.

nominal damages: A token sum (usually one dollar) paid to the plaintiff where legal liability is proven but there are no *actual damages.*

noneconomic damages: Under *HR 3080,* " . . . damages paid to compensate an individual for physical and emotional pain, suffering, inconvenience, physical impairment, mental anguish, disfigurement, loss of enjoyment of life, loss of consortium, and other nonpecuniary losses, but does not include punitive damages."

punitive damages: Money which the defendant is ordered to pay to the plaintiff, the purpose of which is to punish the defendant and discourage the misconduct; these damages are not compensatory. Punitive damages are like the fine imposed for criminal behavior, except that the money is paid to the plaintiff instead of the state. Synonym(s): exemplary damages.
   HR 3080 defines punitive damages as " . . . compensation, in addition to compensation for actual harm suffered, that is awarded for the purpose of punishing a person for conduct deemed to be malicious, wanton, willful, or excessively reckless." When the claim is against the manufacturer of a medical product, no punitive damages may be awarded.

treble damages: Three times the damages (monetary compensation) the plaintiff would otherwise be entitled to. Certain laws permit treble damages as a punitive measure, to discourage certain types of conduct and to encourage injured parties to enforce those laws as "private attorneys general." For example, federal antitrust laws provide for treble damages; the jury's (or judge's) award to a successful plaintiff is tripled. See *Patrick case.*

data bank: See *Health Insurance Coverage Data Bank* and *national fraud and abuse data bank.* See also *data warehouse.*

data interchange system: See *health care data interchange system.*

data set: A specified set of items of information. The data set for a person's address, for example, may be name, street address, city, state, and ZIP code. In the hospital, the term "data set" would be applied, for example, to a discharge abstract and to a patient's bill. In this illustration, the nucleus of both data sets is, at a minimum, the *Uniform Hospital Discharge Data Set (UHDDS)* specified by the federal government (see below).

patient's data set: A computer record of selected data items about an *episode of care*, including identity of the patient, identity of the physician, dates of care, diagnoses, procedures, reference to the original medical record, and other information.

Uniform Clinical Data Set (UCDS): A project of the *Department of Health and Human Services (DHHS)* begun in the late 1980s in an effort to computerize, and thus standardize, the review of Medicare cases by the *Peer Review Organization (PRO)*, and simultaneously to create a clinical research data base. The system involves a nurse or other trained person abstracting some 1,600 clinical data elements from the medical records of cases to be reviewed. These data elements are the input to five algorithms: surgical, disease specific, organ specific, "generic quality screen," and discharge status. The intent of the algorithms is to flag cases which are questionable as to the necessity for admission or the quality of care. Flagged cases are referred to a physician reviewer in the PRO.

The abstracting process for UCDS now requires over an hour to carry out, while cases currently require less than one half hour for "manual" review, working with paper copies of the medical records.

Usage of the term "data set" in this context is unusual, since "data set" ordinarily means simply the array of data elements. Here the term is used to include not only the data elements, but also the entire set of algorithms with which they are to be used, and the computer system required.

Uniform Hospital Discharge Data Set (UHDDS): The items of medical record information required by the federal government as the medical content of the patient's bill under Medicare. Assignment to a *diagnosis related group (DRG)* is made from this data set by the *fiscal intermediary*. UHDDS contains, among other data, patient age, sex, and up to five diagnoses and four procedures. Both diagnoses and procedures are expressed not in words but in the numerical category codes of the *International Classification of Disease, Ninth Revision, Clinical Modification (ICD-9-CM)*.

data repository: See *data warehouse*.

data standards: See *hospital electronic medical data standards*.

data warehouse: An emerging component of integrated computer systems. The data warehouse obtains data from one or more sources and makes it readily available for answering management questions about the organization and its activities. In the hospital, transactions such as patient billing, collecting insurance payments, giving services to patients, purchasing, and others are going on continuously, and access to this flowing stream of data "on-line" in order to obtain management information is awkward and costly. An "off-line" data warehouse system: (1) takes periodic (daily, weekly, monthly) "snapshots" of the computer records coming from these transactions, (2) retains only the data elements of each transaction which are needed for management information (to reduce the bulk of the data and speed the access to it), (3) formats the data in such a fashion that the data from different sources can be handled by the computer as though they were from a single source, (4) stores the data with an eye to ease of access, and (5) provides tools (computer systems) by which the data can be interrogated.

A data warehouse would probably be classified as a "value-added" component of a data system, since it stores and transfers data. The resulting database (or set of relational databases) may be within the hospital or off-site, if the data warehouse operation serves a number of hospitals. A multi-hospital data warehouse not only may offer economies of scale, but it also offers a unique opportunity for exchange of information—governed, of course, by strict security measures for the preservation of confidentiality as to patients, physicians, and institutions. Also called a data repository.

day care: Care, provided by an institution, which does not include an overnight stay; patients reside at night at home or in some other facility.

adult day care: Care, provided during the day, which will permit a patient to function in the home. The care may include a wide range of services-- medical, social, nutritional, psychological, and the like.

DCGs: See *diagnostic cost groups.*

deductible: The amount of money an insured person must pay "at the front end" before the insurer will pay. In automobile collision insurance with a $100 deductible, the insured must pay any damage under $100 in its entirety, and the first $100 when the total is over that amount. The reason for introducing this concept into health care coverage is primarily to discourage "unnecessary" use of services, and also to reduce insurance premiums, since all claims have a "first $100" deductible and the insurer will be spared that amount on every claim. See also *coinsurance* and *copayment.*

defensive medicine: The obtaining of services, mainly diagnostic procedures, in anticipation of defending against a possible lawsuit by the person treated alleging *malpractice.* The primary reasons for obtaining the services is to avoid having to defend against a contention that omission of a test was negligent medical care, and to show the jury in a malpractice trial documented evidence that other possibilities were "ruled out" by the tests.

Ordinarily, diagnostic tests are obtained because the physician honestly needs the information they provide. In defensive medicine, however, the tests have little or no medical value. For example, a physician may be quite satisfied that a sprained ankle is just that; nevertheless, because of the threat of a malpractice suit, may still obtain an X-ray in order to have evidence that a fracture was not overlooked.

definitive care: A level of therapeutic intervention capable of providing comprehensive health care services for a specific condition.

deinstitutionalization: Getting patients out of the hospital and out of other health care institutions and into home or other care.

delivery system: Under *HR 3704,* four delivery systems are considered distinct: " . . . A) Fee-for-service, B) Use of preferred providers; C) Staff or group model health maintenance organizations; and D) such other systems as the Secretary [of Health and Human Services] may recognize."

demarketing: Efforts to persuade individuals not to buy, or to go elsewhere. A hospital has a serious problem when the price set for a given *diagnosis related group (DRG)* under the *prospective payment system (PPS)* is lower than the lowest cost the hospital can achieve for care for a patient with that DRG and still maintain quality. Under those circumstances, the hospital may elect to discontinue caring for such patients (for example, pediatrics). Alternatively, it may develop some more subtle strategy to discourage patients with a *problem* which falls into the DRG from coming to that hospital, or to discourage physicians from bringing such patients. The latter efforts have been labelled "demarketing."

democratization: A trend to put more decision-making into the hands of the individual. A system of health care in which persons collaborate in the decisions about their health and health care is a democratized system.

Department of Health and Human Services (DHHS): The department of the executive branch of the federal government responsible for the federal health programs in the civilian sector, and for Social Security. DHHS is the portion of the Department of Health, Education, and Welfare (DHEW) left after the establishment of the Department of Education as an separate department. DHHS is sometimes referred to as HHS.

DHHS: See *Department of Health and Human Services.*

diagnosis related group (DRG): A hospital patient *classification (1)* system developed under federal grants at Yale University. The current payment system for Medicare is based on the federal government's setting a predetermined price for the "package of care" in the hospital (exclusive of physician's fees) required for each DRG. If the hospital can provide the care for less than the DRG price, it can keep the difference; if the care costs the hospital more than the price, the hospital has to absorb the difference.

Originally each DRG was intended to contain patients who were roughly the same kind of patients in a medical sense and who spent about the same amount of time in the hospital. The groupings were subsequently redefined so that, in addition to medical similarity, resource consumption was approximately the same within a given group.

There are now 468 DRGs identified on the basis of the following criteria: the principal diagnosis (the final diagnosis which, after study in the hospital, was determined to be chiefly responsible for the hospitalization); whether an *operating room procedure* (see *procedure*) was performed; the patient's age; comorbidity; and complication.

A number of efforts are underway to modify DRGs by the use of *severity of illness* measures, and to develop new DRGs for specific classes of patients, as in the case of pediatrics with development of pediatric-modified diagnosis related groups (PM-DRGs). See also *prospective payment system (PPS).*

***Diagnostic and Statistical Manual of Mental Disorders, Third Edition
(DSM-III):*** The definitive *classification (1)* in the U.S. of psychiatric diagnoses, published by the American Psychiatric Association. The first edition
appeared in 1952, the second in 1968, the third in 1980.

diagnostic cost groups (DCGs): A system for paying for hospital care being
tried by the *Health Care Financing Administration (HCFA)* for patients of
Medicare HMOs (see *health maintenance organization (HMO)*). In this system, a patient's prior hospitalization history during the preceding 15
months is used to predict future costs. Prior utilization is expected to
reflect the patient's health status and the physician's practice patterns.
Each patient is placed in one of eight DCGs, depending on costliness, with
the higher number DCGs reflecting higher expected costs to treat the
patient. For each DCG, there is a set of cost weights that depend on the
patient's age, sex, and welfare status. A formula results in the setting of
the HMO's *capitation* rate.

direct care provider: An individual who is responsible for the care of an
individual, as contrasted with a "consultant" who is responsible only for
giving an opinion. However, the consultant may take over the care of the
patient and become the direct care provider.

direct contract: An agreement between an employer and a health care
provider for the provision of health care services to the employees. This is
often referred to as a "direct provider agreement (DPA)."

direct provider agreement (DPA): An agreement between an employer and
a health care provider for the provision of health care services to the
employees.

disability: See *individual with disability.*

discharge: The formal release of a patient from a physician's care or from a
hospital (in Canada, a hospital discharge is called a "separation"). Sometimes called "signing out" the patient. A discharge terminates certain
responsibilities on the part of the *provider.*

discharge planning: The process of making sure that arrangements are made
outside the hospital to receive the patient upon *discharge* and to provide
the necessary continuity of care.

disenrollment: Under *HR 3080,* the removal of an individual from a health
care plan. Restrictions are placed on the rights of an individual to disenroll
"without cause."

disincentive: An undesirable "reward" for undesired behavior. For example, as part of efforts to reduce hospital and physician costs, patients are
sometimes required to pay the first dollars for services; this payment is
called a *deductible.* The deductibles are a "disincentive" (a negative incentive) to seek the care, and thus an *incentive* to be frugal.

disproportionate share hospital (DSH): A Medicare term for a hospital serv-
ing a higher than average proportion of low-income patients.

dispute resolution: See *alternative dispute resolution (ADR).*

diversity action: A lawsuit between citizens of different states. This is one basis of federal rather than state jurisdiction.

divide and dump: To separate high-risk from low-risk employees and "dump" (not insure) the high-risk employees. See *risk (1)*.

donations: In the context of Medicaid financing, donations are money that is "voluntarily" donated to the state government by hospitals and other health providers who receive payments from Medicaid. The money is used by the state for matching with the federal government Medicaid funds. On the average, nearly 60% of a state's Medicaid costs are picked up by the federal matching money, but in some states, the federal share is 80%. In states with 80% matching, one dollar from the state draws $4.00 from the federal level, and thus one dollar of donation from a hospital, for example, will bring it back $5.00.

In some states, a special tax is levied on providers, hospitals and others, rather than asking for or permitting the voluntary donations. Both the donation programs and the special tax programs are under scrutiny, with donations more severely criticized as "scams" rather than legitimate financing mechanisms.

In July 1991, 18 states had either a tax or donation program in place, and another 18 were considering one. In the September 12, 1991, *Federal Register*, the *Health Care Financing Administration (HCFA)* published regulations prohibiting the use of funds "attributable to" taxes imposed solely on providers for matching federal Medicaid funds.

DPA: See *direct provider agreement*.

DPKC: See *Diagnostic Problem-Knowledge Coupler* under *Problem-Knowledge Coupler*.

DRG: See *diagnosis related group*.

DRG coordinator: A hospital employee with duties regarding the *prospective payment system (PPS)*. The duties typically are to: determine at an early date (the first hospital day, if possible) the *diagnosis related group (DRG)* of the patient; inform the attending physician of the normal *length of stay (LOS)* for that DRG and its price; assist in *discharge planning*; and provide feedback from the *case mix management information system (case mix MIS)*; see *information system*.

DRG cost weight: A number, or weight, assigned to each *diagnosis related group (DRG)* by the federal government. It reflects the DRG's use of resources in relation to the cost of the average Medicare patient as determined by the federal government. The average Medicare patient's cost, when multiplied by the DRG cost weight, gives the price for the DRG in question.

DRG creep: A change in the distribution of patients among *diagnosis related group*s (DRGs) without a real change in the distribution of patients treated in the hospital. It is feared that hospitals and physicians will change their record-keeping and reporting so that more patients will appear in higher-priced DRGs, and thus hospital income will be increased without a corresponding increase in cost--the creep will be "upward," and will represent exploitation of the payment system. This term is sometimes inappropriately used when the fact of the matter is that the apparent creep simply represents a systematic improvement in record-keeping and coding. When this is the case, of course, there should be a one-time adjustment, which the PPS system should recognize as laudable.

DRG enhancer: A computer program that assists in extracting and arranging information from the medical record in such a manner as to maximize payment; i.e., put the case into the *diagnosis related group (DRG)* which has the highest price tag. A substantial industry exists which devises and markets these programs.

DRG payment system: Originally, slang for the *prospective payment system (PPS)* of Medicare. However, this term may now be appropriate usage when payment by other than the Medicare program (insurance plans, for example) is also based on *diagnosis related group*s (DRGs).

DRG-specific price blending: See *price blending*.

DRG system: See *prospective payment system (PPS)*.

DSH: See *disproportionate share hospital*.

DSM-III: See *Diagnostic and Statistical Manual of Mental Disorders, Third Edition*.

dumping: The denial or limitation of the provision of medical care to, or the transfer elsewhere of, patients who are not able to pay or for which the payment method (for example, the *prospective payment system (PPS)*) does not pay the hospital enough to cover its costs. Laws intended to prevent dumping typically prohibit the transfer of patients if the transfer cannot be justified by medical necessity. See *Consolidated Omnibus Budget Reconciliation Act of 1985 (COBRA)*. Synonym(s): patient dumping, case shifting.

granny dumping: The practice of abandoning an ill, elderly, indigent person at a hospital or other health care facility.

durable power of attorney: See *advance directive*.

E

EAP: See *employee assistance program*.

Early and Periodic Screening Diagnosis and Treatment Program (EPSDT): A program required of states by Medicaid for children under age 21 in families receiving Aid to Families with Dependent Children (AFDC). EPSDT is designed to detect physical and mental defects and arrange treatment.

early offer: See *alternative dispute resolution*.

Early Resolution Program (ERP): Under the *Health Security Act (HSA)*, programs established in each state, to be administered in each *Complaint Review Office (CRO)* in accordance with regulations issued by the Secretary of Labor, for resolution of disputes related to claims for services denied in full or in part. The procedure is primarily one of mediation. Judicial review is also provided for.

economic credentialing: See *credentialing*.

economic system: The way in which goods and services are produced, distributed, and consumed. In health care, the traditional *provider-driven system* is moving toward a *market-driven system* (see below).

market-driven system: An economic system which responds to the demands of the market, that is, those of the purchaser. The term is currently being applied in health care with the emergence of competitive health care delivery plans which seek to attract "customers" by offering (1) more of what the customers want (amenities as well as services) or (2) attractive prices (that is, price competition). Note that the *customer* is the person paying for the service, and is not necessarily the *consumer* (the patient).

provider-driven system: An economic system in which *providers* (in health care, physicians, other professionals, and institutions) "prescribe" and furnish those services which they consider to be the best care for the patients. Such a system is intended to meet the needs of the patients as determined by the providers rather than to meet the demands of the purchasers of care.

effectiveness: The degree to which the effort expended, or the action taken, achieves the desired effect (result or objective). For example, one drug is more effective than another if it relieves certain symptoms to a greater extent, or in a higher proportion of patients. See also *efficiency*, which is often confused with effectiveness. Synonym(s): efficacy.

efficacy: See *effectiveness*.

efficiency: The relationship of the amount of work accomplished to the amount of effort required. A given hospital's food service is more efficient than another hospital's in one measure if, for example, it can furnish meals to patients for a lower average cost per meal (assuming that the meals are of equal quality). Although efficiency is usually thought of in terms of cost, it can equally well be measured in other ways, such as time; for example, the automobile racing crew which can change a set of tires in the shortest time is the most efficient. See also *effectiveness*, which is often confused with efficiency.

elder care: Home care of the elderly by relatives. Tax relief for families who provide home health care for an elderly relative has been proposed. Relief has also been proposed for families who care for a dependent suffering from Alzheimer's disease.

elective: A term that refers to treatment which is medically advisable, but not critical. Elective care (such as hospitalization, treatment, or surgery) can be scheduled in advance, in contrast to emergency care, which must be rendered immediately to avoid death or serious disability.

eligible employee: Under *HR 3080* and *HR 3704*, "with respect to an employer, an employee who normally performs on a monthly basis at least 30 hours of service per week for that employer."

eligible individual: Under *HR 3080*, "with respect to an eligible employee, such employee, and any dependent of such employee."

eligibility: A term usually used in health care with reference to whether an individual is entitled to specific *benefits*, or may be covered at all, under a given insurance plan, governmental program, or other *health care plan*.

eligibility period: The period of time a new employee has to sign up for life or health insurance without having to take a physical examination or otherwise show insurability. After the eligibility period has expired, the employee may be denied insurance because of a *preexisting condition*, or have to pay higher premiums.

emergency: A situation requiring immediate attention in order to prevent death or severe disability. A situation less critical is "urgent." The least critical level is "elective."

employee assistance program (EAP): An occupational health service program to help employees with substance abuse or physical or behavioral problems deal with these problems when they affect job performance. The assistance may be provided within the organization or by referral to outside resources.

employee health benefit plan: An organization's plan for health benefits for its employees and their dependents. The term generally refers to the "package" of benefits which are provided. Such plans are among the "fringe benefits" of the employees, and thus are not part of the employee's salary. The employees may or may not contribute to paying the cost by deductions from their salaries.

Employee Retirement Income Security Act (ERISA): A 1974 federal act which preempts states rights with regard to workers' pension benefits and employee benefits. ERISA does not affect the benefits and rights of employees whose employer is self-insured.

employer mandate: See *mandate*.

empowerment: See *patient empowerment*.

encounter: The personal contact between the patient and a professional health care giver. This term is typically used only with respect to personnel involved in assessment or treatment, or providing social services, not with obtaining a prescription drug from a pharmacy, for example.

enrollee: As used in health insurance and with prepayment plans, a person who is covered under a contract for care. The holder of the contract is called the *subscriber*. An enrollee may or may not be a dependent of the subscriber.

enrollee unit: Under *HR 3222*, " . . . one unit in the case of coverage on an individual basis or in the case of coverage on a family basis."

enterprise liability: The term used in the *Health Security Act (HSA)* for *organizational liability*; see *liability (1)*.

EPI: See *Estes Park Institute*.

episode of care: A continuous course of care by a hospital or physician for a specific medical *problem* or condition. Often the term has a specific definition under a federal or state statute.

EPO: See *exclusive provider organization*.

EPSDT: See *Early and Periodic Screening Diagnosis and Treatment Program*.

equivalent health care program: Under *HR 3704*, any of the existing programs, Medicare, Medicaid, the other programs operated by the federal government, and "any other plan recognized by the Secretary [of Health and Human Services] the purpose of which is to provide retiree health benefits."

ERISA: See *Employee Retirement Income Security Act*.

ERP: See *Early Resolution Program*.

essential community provider: Under the *Health Security Act (HSA)*, certain providers would automatically be so certified: migrant health centers, community health centers, homeless program providers, public housing providers, family planning clinics, Indian health programs, AIDS providers under the Ryan White Act, maternal and child health providers, federally qualified health centers, rural health clinics, providers of school health services, and community practice networks. In addition, the Secretary of Health and Human Services (HHS) may give the certification to health professionals, institutional providers such as hospitals, and other public and private nonprofit agencies and organizations that are in areas which have been designated as health professional shortage areas, or which are providing a substantial amount of service to a population which has been designated as medically underserved.

Estes Park Institute (EPI): An independent nonprofit corporation providing education and other services for the health care community. EPI's main programs are national conferences for hospital medical staff organization (MSO) officers, hospital and other health care administrator and trustees, and their spouses. Estes Park Institute, P.O. Box 400, Englewood, CO 80151. Telephone 800-223-4430.

Eutaw Group: An ad hoc health care "think tank" with William F. Bridgers, MD, as Head. Bridgers is founding Dean of the School of Public Health of the University of Alabama. The Eutaw Group contends that the health care universe is one comprised of "haves" and "havenots," and that this distinction is more important than the usual distinction into urban and rural. As a result, the Eutaw Group proposes a *community care plan* as an alternative (or complement) to the *accountable health plan (AHP)* for the underserved populations, both urban and rural. Bridgers is the author of *Health Care*

Reform: A Dilemma and a Pathway for the Health Care System (1992), which is available at local bookstores. Eutaw Group, 2221 English Village Lane, Birmingham, AL 35223. Telephone 205-879-0365.

exclusive provider organization (EPO): An *alternative delivery system (ADS)* for health care which is a cross between a *health maintenance organization (HMO)* and a *preferred provider organization (PPO)*. As in PPOs, the *providers* are paid on a *fee-for-service* basis and generally the providers are not at risk (see *risk (2)*). However, beneficiaries have less freedom in obtaining their care from providers outside the panel than they do in PPOs (where other providers may be employed by the patient, but at some financial penalty).

expenditure target: A goal for attempting to hold down the rate of growth in expenditures. Such a target may be mandated by law and limit the payments which may be made, for example, to a physician in a given year. One such target is the *Medicare Volume Performance Standards (MVPS)*.

experience rating: See *rating*.

explicit: Specifically stated. For example, if there are conditions tied to one's income which state that nothing can be spent on travel, that is an *explicit* limitation. If there are no conditions, but the income will not permit both a vacation trip and painting the house, the necessity for choice (or establishing priorities) is *implicit*; it goes "naturally" with the idea of limited funds.

In financing medical and hospital care, limited funds require choices as to how to spend them. In the past, the *rationing* of funds has been implicit, but some states are beginning to use explicit methods; see *Oregon plan*.

external independent review: See *review*.

extraordinary treatment: See *treatment*.

F

FAAHC: Fellow of the *American Association of Healthcare Consultants*.

family share: Under the *Health Security Act (HSA)*, a portion of the health insurance premium is to be paid by the family, the family share, and a portion by the employer. Methods are presented for calculation of each share, taking into account such factors as "class" of enrollment and whether or not the family receives Aid for Dependent Children (AFDC) or Social Security Insurance (SSI). Adjustments are to be made for low income families.

FASB: See *Financial Accounting Standards Board*.

federal alternative dispute resolution system (ADR system): Under *HR 3080*, to be established by the Secretary of Health and Human Services, in consultation with the Attorney General, to be available for states which have not such systems which have been certified by the Secretary. (See *alternative dispute resolution (ADR)*.)

Federal Employees Health Benefits Program (FEHBP, FEP): A voluntary group health insurance program for federal employees.

Federal Health Plan Review Board (FHPRB): Under the *Health Security Act (HSA)*, a 5-member body responsible to the Secretary of Labor, charged with reviewing the decisions of *Complaint Review Office (CRO)* hearing officers as to complaints when an appeal is filed.

Federal Trade Commission (FTC): A federal agency which has jurisdiction over unfair and deceptive trade practices. Some such practices may violate the federal *antitrust* laws. The FTC was created in 1914 by the Federal Trade Commission Act (15 U.S.C. sec. 45 (1982)).

federalism: A form of association between organizations which are independent but which delegate certain common functions to a central body. The United States is a federation. There is increasing interest in forming local federations among health care providers and agencies in order to allow organizations and institutions to retain their identities and yet to avoid duplication and thus to meet the unique health care needs of the individual community in the most appropriate and economical fashion.

federally qualified health centers and rural health centers: Under *HR 3704*, these are (with detailed definitions) migrant health centers, community health centers, homeless program providers, public housing providers, family planning clinics, Indian Health program, AIDS providers under the Ryan-White Act, maternal and child health providers, federally qualified health centers, and rural health clinics.

fee: A *charge* for a *service* rendered.

fee-for-service (FFS): A method of paying physicians and other health care providers in which each *service* (for example, a doctor's office visit or operation) carries a *fee*. The physician's income under this system is made up from the fees she or he collects for services. Alternative methods of income for physicians are: (1) a salary, such as one paid by a *health maintenance organization (HMO)*; and (2) a *capitation* payment system, in which the physician is paid a predetermined amount for each patient for which she or he assumes responsibility (rather than for each service rendered) during a given period of time. Note that the capitation method can be applied via some type of organization, for example, an HMO; in that case the capitation payment is made to the HMO, which in turn pays the physician in the manner decided by the HMO.

fee schedule: A list of *charge*s (or allowances) for specific *procedure*s and *service*s.

FEHBP: See *Federal Employee Health Benefit Program*.

FEP: See *Federal Employee Health Benefit Program*.

FFS: See *fee-for-service*.

FHPRB: See *Federal Health Plan Review Board*.

Financial Accounting Standards Board (FASB): A professional group which establishes standards for record-keeping, performance, reporting, and ethics for the accounting profession.

financing: A method of paying for health care ("health care financing").

first-dollar coverage: Insurance which has no *copayment* or *deductible* provision; the insured does not have to pay the first dollar--the insurer pays it.

fiscal intermediary: An agency, usually a Blue Cross Plan or private insurance company, selected by health care providers to pay claims under Medicare. Sometimes referred to simply as "intermediary."

501(c)(*): Section 501(section)(numbered paragraph) of the United States Internal Revenue Code of 1954 (as subsequently amended). Section 501(c) is the section dealing with nonprofit organizations exempt from federal income taxes. Any organization, to qualify for tax-exempt status under the Internal Revenue Code, must be incorporated in a given state as a nonprofit organization. Such incorporation, of itself, is not sufficient to grant exemption from federal income taxes. This exemption is granted only if the IRS, following application by the organization, makes a "determination" that the organization is properly qualified under a specific paragraph. Each numbered paragraph deals with a "class" of such qualified nonprofit organizations. For example, "501(c)(1) organizations" are those exempt from income taxes because they have been organized under Acts of Congress; "501(c)(16)" organizations are those organized to finance crop operations.

Three classes of organizations in health care find the 501(c)(*) classification of particular interest at this time for two primary reasons: (1) relief from income taxes gives all of them a substantial savings, and (2) for those qualifying for 501(c)(3) classification ("501(c)(3) organizations"), the ability to obtain tax-deductible contributions from foundations and individuals may provide significant income. The three classifications are:

501(c)(3): The classification reserved for nonprofit organizations which are one or more of the following: primarily those that are charitable, scientific, religious, or educational. Nonprofit hospitals fall into this category, as do churches, and educational institutions. 501(c)(3) organizations are able to obtain tax-deductible donations from individuals and grants from foundations (foundations ordinarily are not able to make grants to organizations, even though the organizations are nonprofit, unless the grantee has obtained this designation from the IRS). Foundations routinely request evidence that the applicant has obtained the 501(c)(3) determination from the IRS.

501(c)(4): The classification for nonprofit organizations which, while they may be similar to hospitals in many respects, do not satisfy the IRS that they are charitable. HMOs and PHOs typically are given this classification. They are then exempt from paying federal income taxes (this results in a substantial reduction in their operating costs), but contributions to them are not tax-deductible to the donor. Thus they are ineligible for grants from foundations and tax-deductible gifts from individuals.

501(c)(6): The classification typically described as that for nonprofit "trade associations." State and national professional associations, such as those of physicians, and associations of organizations, such as hospitals, usually qualify for this classification.

501(c)(3) corporation: A *nonprofit* organization which has been granted a "determination" by the Internal Revenue Service (IRS) that it meets the requirements under Section 501(c)(3) of the *Internal Revenue Code* for classification as "scientific, educational, religious, or charitable," and thus is exempt from federal income taxes, and may receive donations which are "tax-deductible" to the donating individual, foundation, or corporation (see *tax-exempt* and *tax deduction*). Such status is often required by organizations which give grants.

flexible spending account (FSA): An account managed by an employer that allows employees to set aside pretax funds for medical, dental, legal, and day-care services. FSAs may be components of "cafeteria plans" for providing health care which allow employees to choose among various levels of *benefits*. See *Zero Balanced Reimbursement Account (ZEBRA)*.

FMC: See *foundation for medical care*.

forms 1007 and 1008: Forms used in the Medicare *prospective payment system (PPS)* to calculate a hospital's adjustments to its *base year Medicare costs*.

foundation for medical care (FMC): A nonprofit organization, usually of physicians, that provides *medical services review* or *utilization review* (see *review*) of a specific population under a *prepayment* contract for health care.

fraud: Obtaining products, services, or reimbursement by intentional false statements. Fraud includes such acts as misrepresenting eligibility or need for services, and claiming reimbursement for services not rendered or for nonexistent patients. Fraud is illegal and may carry civil and criminal penalties. Medicare law specifically prohibits fraud; see *fraud and abuse*.

fraud and abuse: The criminal misuse of the Medicare system. The crime consists of such behavior as filing false claims for Medicare reimbursement (such as for nonexistent patients, or services that were never performed), paying or receiving "kickbacks" for patient referral, and so forth. Fraud and abuse is a felony which may be punished by fines up to $25,000 or five years in prison, or both, and automatic suspension from participation in Medicare and Medicaid. 42 U.S.C. sec. 1395nn(b). See also *abuse* and *safe harbor regulations*.

fraud and abuse data bank: See *national fraud and abuse data bank*.

freedom-of-choice: A policy which permits patients to choose their own physicians. Such choice is at least restricted for persons who are members of an HMO or other managed care plan, because they must go to physicians within the plan (or themselves pay for care obtained elsewhere). In some HMOs patients must be satisfied with the physician on call.

freedom-of-choice waiver: A waiver which excuses the purchaser of care from permitting freedom of choice to the beneficiaries. Freedom of choice is a normal requirement for Medicaid; a state, for example, wishing to carry out its Medicaid plan via managed care would need such a waiver.

frontier states: Under *HR 3704*, include Alaska, Wyoming, and Montana.

FSA: See *flexible spending account.*

FTC: See *Federal Trade Commission.*

futile care: A circumstance in which treatment, other than *comfort care*, could not, in the opinion of the physician (and, usually, consultants) reasonably be expected to result in a quality of life which would be acceptable to the patient.

futility policy: A hospital policy dealing with the issues presented by *futile care.*

G

gaming: Attempting to manipulate "the system" in an illegal or unethical manner. The terms "gaming" and "to game the system" are used, for example, in connection with efforts to bill under the *prospective payment system (PPS)* in such a way as to maximize income by giving as the principal diagnosis that diagnosis which places the patient in the highest-priced *diagnosis related group (DRG)*, even though a lower-priced one more correctly reflects the patient's *problem* and the services rendered.

gatekeeper: See *patient care manager (PCM).*

gateway: See *patient care manager (PCM).*

GDP: See *gross domestic product.*

general access health care plan: See *health care plan.*

General Health Policy Model (GHPM): A method of expressing the benefits of health programs in a common unit known as the *well-year.*

Gephardt bill (HR 3600): See *Health Security Act (HSA).*

German-style system: A regulated *multipayer system* of health care. In Germany, approximately 1200 nonprofit insurance plans, called *Krankenkasse* or "sickness funds," are organized by employers, labor unions, and professional groups. The plans are funded by equal payroll taxes on both employers and employees. Self-employed and wealthier employees may purchase private insurance. Funds are turned over to regional networks of physicians, who reimburse doctors in private practice, and to hospitals, who pay their staff physicians. Physician networks oversee their members' utilization. The government oversees fee negotiations (see *negotiated fee* *schedule*) which set global budgets, and also covers the poor and the unemployed.

GHPM: See *General Health Policy Model.*

global budgeting: A limit on total health care spending for a given unit of population, taking into account all sources of funds. In the health care reform discussions and proposals, it is not clear how the information as to the total spending data is to be obtained or the "cap" will be enforced, but suggestions are that there will be caps (1) on employers expenditures, based on payroll, (2) on individual expenditures for insurance, based on income, (3) on institutional budgets' "core spending," and (4) on personal out-of-pocket expenditures.

GNP: See *gross national product.*

going bare: Slang for practicing without professional liability (malpractice) insurance coverage.

granny dumping: See *dumping.*

gross domestic product (GDP): The market value of all goods and services produced by labor and property *within* the U.S. during a particular period of time. Income from overseas operations of a domestic corporation would *not* be included in the GDP, but activities carried on within U.S. borders by a foreign company would be. The GDP measures "how the U.S. economy" is doing.

In 1991, the GDP replaced the *gross national product (GNP)* to bring the U.S. into greater conformity with international measures of national income.

gross national product (GNP): The market value of all goods and services produced by labor and property supplied *by residents of* the U.S. during a particular period of time. Income from overseas operations of a domestic corporation would be included in the GNP, which measures "how U.S. residents" are doing economically. See *gross domestic product (GDP).*

GROUPER: A specific computer program (logic) by which patient bills under Medicare are classified to their *diagnosis related groups (DRGs)*, using the *Uniform Hospital Discharge Data Set (UHDDS)* (see *data set*) which contains up to five diagnoses and four *procedures* coded by the *International Classification of Diseases, 9th Revision, Clinical Modification (ICD-9-CM)* along with other standardized information about the patient.

guaranty fund: A pool of money, funded by assessing insurers, which is designed to protect health care providers and consumers if an insurer becomes insolvent.

guidelines (1): Statements of suggested policies or procedures.

administrative guidelines: Suggestions promulgated by an administrative *agency* as to procedure or interpretations of law. Guidelines are less binding than *regulations*, which have the force of law.

health planning guidelines: A set of guidelines, issued by the U.S. *Department of Health and Human Services (DHHS)* in response to 1974 federal legislation, to assist state and local health planning agencies with their activities and policies.

guidelines (2): Practice guidelines; also called practice parameters, guidelines for medical care, Clinical Practice Guidelines. These are statements by authoritative bodies as to the procedures appropriate for the physician to employ in making a given diagnosis and treating it. They are intended to change providers' practice styles, reduce inappropriate and unnecessary care, and cut costs. It is also proposed that they may "streamline the process of settling medical malpractice claims."

The *Agency for Health Care Policy and Research (AHCPR)* has been charged with responsibility for producing "Clinical Practice Guidelines (CPGs), and has issued a number of them. A number of medical associations and specialty societies, as well as hospitals, have also published guidelines for various kinds of patients.

The first guidelines were for the management of a given diagnosis or of the treatment planned. More recently, other topics pertaining to health have appeared, for example, "Driving Following a Single Seizure."

The term "guidelines" has not been well-received by the American Medical Association (AMA), which prefers "practice parameters," apparently because "guidelines" has been used for governmental pronouncements, which appear more legally binding. An AMA spokesperson has stated ". . . practice parameters are not like laws; they're published in journals, and it's up to each person to keep current about what's going on."

At least 2,000 guidelines are now in print, although a recent issue of the AMA publication *Practice Parameters Update*, which listed about 100 newly published parameters, also listed about 35 parameters which had been withdrawn during the same period. So the number of and titles of those "in force" is constantly changing.

Guidelines may not be the answer to controlling or improving quality, or controlling cost. Guidelines must necessarily be so broad that they will only identify extreme *under-* and *over-*utilization for a given diagnosis or procedure, or disclose conspicuously egregious practice. There is no way they can be tailored to the individual patient. They also raise serious questions with regard to malpractice, just a few of which are: (1) Is it OK to do *everything* in a guideline? (2) *Must* one do everything within a guideline? (3) If one stays within a guideline does this grant immunity from malpractice? (4) What if a guideline is withdrawn (as about one-third of them are) and a physician still follows it?

For potentially better solutions, see *critical path* and *Problem-Knowledge Coupler.*

H

HA: See *health alliance.*

HAD: See *health care alternatives development.*

Hawaii plan: The "health care reform" plan instituted in Hawaii in 1974 with passage of a law which required *all* employers to provide health insurance for all employees working 20 hours a week or more. For the indigent and Medicaid, the insurance is subsidized by the government. Something over 95% of Hawaiians are covered by health insurance vs. about 85% on the mainland. Hawaiians claim "near-universal" coverage. The Hawaii plan is advanced by some as a model for the entire U.S., citing Hawaii's lower spending for health care (9% vs. 13% for the U.S. as a whole, despite a higher cost of living in Hawaii) and its statistical evidence, such as lower rates of hospitalization and lower death rates for certain condition. Critics insist that we must lower our costs before we can provide as extensive coverage and achieve better health, while Hawaiian advocates claim that the greater coverage in Hawaii provides preventive care which is the cause of the lower costs. Critics also fault Hawaii for the uninsured population which still exists there, and the "makeshift" efforts to close the gap. Hawaii is held up as a model of the successful financing of health care by "employer mandate," a financing mechanism under consideration in the reform discussions (sometimes referred to as "pay or play"). See *employer mandate* under *mandate.*

HCCA: See *health care coverage area.*

HCDP: See *Health Care Data Panel.*

HCFA: See *Health Care Financing Administration.*

HCI: See *Health Commons Institute.*

HCO: See *health care organization.*

HCPR: Health Care Policy and Research. See *Agency for Health Care Policy and Research (AHCPR).*

HealSB: See *Health Standards Board.*

health: As defined by the World Health Organization (WHO), "the extent to which an individual or group is able, on the one hand, to develop aspirations and satisfy needs; and, on the other hand, to change or cope with the environment. Health is therefore seen as a resource for everyday life, not the objective of living; it is seen as a positive concept emphasizing social and personal resources, as well as physical capacities." In common usage, "health" often is used to refer to the condition of physical, mental, and social well-being, and is much like the word "quality" in that it is modified by adjectives in such phrases as "poor health," "good health," or "failing health." It is worth noting that increasing attention is being given to *quality of life.*

health alliance (HA): An organization proposed to be established in the *managed competition* approach to health care reform to serve as a "sponsor" for populations which would otherwise have no intermediary between their beneficiaries and organizations which provide care. Its basic functions are to bargain with and purchase health insurance from *accountable health plans* (AHPs) or other sources of health care in behalf of consumers, and to furnish information to consumers on the services provided by the competing AHPs, an evaluation of their quality of care, participant satisfaction, and price.

Health alliances are not needed for groups such as corporations with many employees, state governments, and similar institutions which are large enough effectively to carry out the purchasing function themselves.

When proposed initially, the organization was called a "health insurance purchasing corporation (HIPC)." This was then changed to "health insurance purchasing cooperative (HIPC)" and, later, "health plan purchasing cooperative (HPPC)." All were referred to as "HICK-PIX," an acronym no one could look up in a glossary. Another recent synonym is "insurance purchasing pool." The current terminology seems to be settling to "health alliance."

Under the *Health Security Act (HSA),* there are two kinds of health alliances: regional health alliances and corporate health alliances (see below). When used by itself, "alliance" usually refers to a regional health alliance.

corporate health alliance: Under the *Health Security Act (HSA),* (1) a large employer, (2) a [large] multiemployer plan as specified under the *Employee Retirement Income Security Act (ERISA),* or (3) a large rural electric or telephone cooperative. In each instance, the word "large" means more than 5,000 employees or participants.

regional health alliance, regional alliance: Under the *Health Security Act (HSA),* a nonprofit corporation, or an independent state agency, or a state agency which meets the requirements of the Act and carries out the activities called for under the Act.

health allowance program: See *State health allowance program.*

health care: Services of health care professionals and their agents which are addressed at: (1) *health promotion;* (2) prevention of illness and injury; (3) monitoring of *health;* (4) maintenance of health; and (5) treatment of diseases, disorders, and injuries in order to obtain cure or, failing that, optimum comfort and function (*quality of life*).

health care alternatives development (HAD): A term that refers to the development of *alternative delivery systems* and *alternative financing systems.* One must seek the context of this term to understand just what is meant.

health care coalition: An organization working on broad health care concerns, ordinarily including hospital and health care costs, and typically with *provider*, business, and *consumer* participation. Often there is government participation as well.

business health care coalition: A health care coalition comprised of or organized by business firms concerned with health care problems, primarily those problems affecting employees of the member companies. Such a coalition is also likely to have *providers* and *consumers* as members.

Health Care Competition Policy: See *Office of Health Care Competition Policy*.

health care coverage area (HCCA): Under *HR 3704*, a geographical area within which a health care plan agrees to provide health care.

health care data interchange system: Under *HR 3704*, a system to make health care data available on a uniform basis to all participants in the health care system. The system shall (1) include all participants, (2) use uniform electronic processes, (3) protect the privacy of individuals, (4) ensure "that the data in the system is verifiable, timely, accurate, reliable, useful, complete, relevant, time and date stamped, and comparable, and (5) [ensure] an overall reduction in the administrative burdens and costs of the health care system, an overall increase in the productivity, effectiveness, and efficiency of the system, and an overall increase in the quality of care furnished by the system."

Health Care Data Panel (HCDP): Under *HR 3704*, a body of 15 federal officers under with the Secretary [of Health and Human Services] as Chair, which is, in general, in charge of the *health care data interchange system*.

health care delivery: A term sometimes used as a synonym for "comprehensive health care delivery system." However, the term "health care delivery" applies to providing any of the wide array of *health care* services as well as to the totality.

health care delivery system: A term without specific definition, referring to all the facilities and services, along with methods for financing them, through which health care is provided.

health care expenses advance amount: Under *HR 1743*, an amount paid by an employer to an employee for an employee who has given the employer evidence that he is eligible for health expenses credit. The amount is determined by a formula in the Act, and is equal to the health care expenses credit.

health care expenses credit: Under *HR 1743*, a tax credit allowed an individual for health expenses [defined] against the "refundable personal credits" allowed by the IRS.

Health Care Financing Administration (HCFA): The division of the *Department of Health and Human Services (DHHS)* which administers the Medicare and Medicaid programs at the federal level.

health care information clearinghouse: Under *HR 3704*, " . . . a public or private entity that A) processes data that cannot be sent directly due to lack of proper formatting or editing; and B) facilitates the translation of data to the standardized data set and code sets between persons who normally would send or receive the transaction; but does not store information processed beyond the time required to complete its task and communicate the information."

health care organization (HCO): An organizational form for health care delivery in which the financial risk (see *risk (2)*) is assumed by the organization, rather than by individuals.

health care plan: An organized service to provide stipulated medical, hospital, and related services (*benefits*) to individuals under a *prepayment* contract. The plan may be offered by a *Blue Cross/Blue Shield (BC/BS)* plan, an insurance company, a *health maintenance organization (HMO)*, a *health care organization (HCO)*, or other organization. See also *accountable health plan (AHP)* and *prepaid health plan*.

general access health care plan: Under *HR 3704*, a health plan set up under the Act for the small employer and individual marketplace. Initial responsibility for development of the necessary standards for such plans is delegated to the National Association of Insurance Commissioners (NAIC); with the Secretary [of Health and Human Services] to develop the standards if the NAIC fails to do a satisfactory job.

Health Care Policy and Research: See *Agency for Health Care Policy and Research (AHCPR)*.

health care professional: Under *HR 3080*, "... any individual who provides health care services in a State and who is required . . . to be licensed or certified by the State . . . " (See also *health professional*.)

licensed health care professional: Under *HR 3080*, "... any physician . . . any registered professional nurse, licensed social worker, or other individual who meets such requirements as may be prescribed by the Secretary [of Health and Human Services]."

health care provider: Under *HR 3080*, " . . . any organization or institution that is engaged in the delivery of health care services . . . and that is required to be licensed or certified . . . "

health care proxy: See *advance directive*.

health care reform: A term without a clear definition, which is applied to the current (1993) efforts on the federal, state, and local levels to make changes in the health care delivery system so that (1) costs are reduced or "contained," (2) the uninsured population, estimated as 35-40 million people nationally, are covered; (3) all citizens have access to health care, (4) financing is assured, and (5) quality of care is controlled or, preferably, improved. The proposal from the *Task Force on National Health Reform* is expected to couple *managed competition* with *global budgeting* which provides a cap on health care costs. The options as to "management" of the health care system range from highly centralized, federal controls to the setting of certain requirements at the federal level but allowing local innovation as to implementation.

Health Care Standards Commission (Commission): Under *HR 3222*, an independent agency in the Executive Branch composed of 5 members with the duty of recommending to Congress the specifications of the uniform set of benefits to be provided enrollees. The benefits will include medically appropriate treatments, clinical preventive services, and diagnostic services. Practice guidelines may be developed which may specify the appropriate uses of treatment in greater detail. ("Specialty clinical practice guidelines," to be developed under *HR 3704*, may be introduced as a rebuttable presumption that the service . . . is the appropriate standard of care . . . "). (See *rebuttable presumption*.)

health care system: A system designed to take responsibility only for the *care* of those who seek it out. It responds to the needs of individual patients who present themselves with illness or injury. This is in contrast with with a *health* system (see *health system*).

health care training consortium: Under *HR 3704*, " . . . a State, regional, or local entity which A) includes teaching hospitals, ambulatory training sites, and one or more schools of medicine located in the same geographic region; and B) is operated in a manner intended to insure that at least 50% of the graduates . . . will become primary care providers during the 1-year period immediately following the date such graduates complete their residency training."

health care value-added network: Under *HR 3704*, " . . . any entity that provides additional services beyond the transmission of data or value, such as the storage of electronic data or value and the transfer of such data or value between health care entities."

health care value information: Under *HR 1743*, this appears to mean price information, although in the future, information systems are to " . . . provide comparative costs, quality, and outcomes data . . . "

Health Commons Institute (HCI): A nonprofit corporation dedicated to applying modern information technology at the person-health care system clinical interface. The primary such interface is the patient-physician encounter and relationship. The name of the organization was derived from the concept of a "commons" as a meeting ground.

HCI was established in 1992 as a result of the beliefs of its founders and others that the potential now exists for a true *paradigm shift* in health care, characterized in part by a change in the locus of control of health care and decision making from doctors toward patients and their families. Trends supporting this belief include: (1) today's Americans increasingly want to make their own choices in matters of health and health care; (2) wise choices can only be made where complete, but patient- and problem- specific, information is available and intelligible at the place and time of decision making; (3) only through modern information technology (i.e., the computer) is it possible to meet this information requirement (the volume of biomedical literature is overwhelming) (see *Problem-Knowledge Coupler* as an example of an approach to this problem); and (4) "patients" often need the help of the health care professional in the analysis of their problems, in interpretation of the biomedical information, and in making choices among their options as to health promotion, disease prevention, health problem solution, and therapy.

HCI's mission is to study and facilitate this paradigm shift with respect to: physician (and other professional) education; patient education; public education; health care practice design; health care cost; effects on personal health; community health outcomes achieved; public health practice; legal implications for information technology, licensure, and *tort* considerations; computer hardware and software application and development; library and other information management; medical record systems.

Health Commons Institute, 50 Monument Square, Suite 502, Portland, ME 04101. Telephone 207-874-6552.

Health Deduction Fairness: Under *HR 3080*, Subtitle D, under this heading, increases the percentage of the health insurance cost for self-employed individuals when the insurance purchased meets certain standards.

health economics: The branch of economics which deals with the provision of health care services, their delivery, and their use, with special attention to quantifying the demands for such services, the costs of such services and of their delivery, and the benefits obtained. More emphasis is given to the costs and benefits of health care to a population than to the individual.

Health Equity and Access Reform Today Act of 1993 (HEART) (S 1770 & HR 3704): The health care reform bill introduced in the Senate by Senator Chafee (S 1770). Its companion bill in the House of Representatives was introduced by Representative Thomas (HR 3704).

health expenses credit: See *health care expenses credit*.

Health Insurance Coverage Data Bank: Under *HR 3704*, a national mandatory data bank into which must be deposited (with some exceptions) information about each individual insured under the Act each year.

health insurance plan (HIP): Under *HR 3080*, with certain exceptions, " . . . any hospital or medical service policy or certificate, hospital or medical service plan contract, or health maintenance organization group contract offered by an insurer."

health insurance purchasing cooperative (HIPC): See *health alliance (HA)*.

Health Insurance Standards Board (HISB): One of three advisory boards to the *National Health Board (NHB)* proposed by the *Jackson Hole Group*. The HISB, if the proposal is implemented, will set "standards for HPPCs [health plan purchasing cooperatives; see *health alliance (HA)*]; will develop model state laws and regulations working with the NAIC [*National Association of Insurance Commissioners*]; will set the standards AHPs [*accountable health plans*] must meet with respect to underwriting and business practices, phased-in schedule for enrollment, and managed care requirements. Will advise on implementation of *Uniform Effective Health Benefits* [UEHB] coverage. Will consist of insurance, employer, consumer, and health provider group representatives."

Health Insurance Trust Fund (HITF): The federal fund which pays for Part A (the hospital portion) of Medicare.

health IRA: See *individual health care account.*

health maintenance: All efforts carried out in order to preserve *health.* As used in the term *health maintenance organization (HMO),* however, the term is not so inclusive, but rather simply includes those efforts which are required under the contract between the subscriber (person enrolled) and the HMO.

health maintenance organization (HMO): A health care providing organization which ordinarily has a closed group ("panel") of physicians (and sometimes other health care professionals), along with either its own hospital or allocated beds in one or more hospitals. Individuals (usually families) "join" an HMO, which agrees to provide "all" the medical and hospital care they need, for a fixed, predetermined fee. Actually, each subscriber (person enrolled) is under a contract stipulating the limits of the service (not "all" the care needed). Such a contract is called a "risk contract" (see *risk (2)),* and the HMO is therefore called a "risk contractor."

social/health maintenance organization (S/HMO): A newer type of *long-term care (LTC)* "alternative" organization under experimentation in which one provider, under a *capitation* payment (a fixed fee for each individual covered), furnishes both social and health care services for (currently) low income individuals.

health outcome: Under *HR 3222,* " . . . an outcome that affects the length or quality of an enrollee's life."

health plan: Under the *Health Security Act (HSA),* an organization which provides the comprehensive benefit package spelled out in HSA, and which is either a "self-insured plan" under the provisions of the *Employee Retirement Income Security Act (ERISA)* or a plan that has been certified by the state or the *National Health Board (NHB).* HSA as written has the ability to preempt state laws which would place certain specified restrictions on health plans under the Act. See also *health care plan* and *accountable health plan.*

qualified health plan: Under *HR 3704,* a specifically defined entity.

supplemental health plan (SHP): Under the *Health Security Act (HSA),* a health insurance plan which provides coverage for items and services which are not in the *comprehensive benefit package (CBP)* or items and services which are excluded from the CBP by statute.

Health Plan Standards Board (HPSB): Under *HR 3222,* a nonprofit corporation under a board of directors of 5 members. Its functions are to (1) advise the *Health Care Standards Commission* concerning standards for *accountable health plans* (AHPs) (other than those relating to the uniform set of effective benefits and the national health data system) and for Health Plan Purchasing Cooperatives (HPPCs); and (2) assess the "risk-adjustment factors" called for by the Act.

health plan purchasing cooperative (HPPC): See *health alliance (HA).*

Health Policy Agenda for the American People (HPA): A program spearheaded by the American Medical Association (AMA) to develop a set of proposals for improving health and health care in America. Among organizations sending representatives to HPA were the American Association of Retired Persons (AARP), American Nurses Association (ANA), Blue Cross and Blue Shield Association (BC/BSA), Business Roundtable, Health Insurance Association of America (HIAA), U.S. Chamber of Commerce, and various state and national medical and specialty associations. Completion of the agenda development was accomplished in 1986. A summary giving the 195 recommendations was published in early 1987 in the *Journal of the American Medical Association (JAMA)*.

health professional: Under the *Health Security Act (HSA)*, means a physician, nurse, nurse practitioner, certified nurse midwife, physician assistant, psychologist, dentist, pharmacist, and other health care professional recognized by the Secretary of Health and Human Services (HHS). (See also *health care professional.*)

health professional shortage area: An area so designated by the Secretary of Health and Human Services (HHS) under the Public Health Service Act.

health promotion: Efforts to change peoples' behavior in order to promote healthy lives and, to the extent possible, prevent illnesses and accidents and to minimize their effects, rather than having people use the health care system for "repairs." A health promotion program may include health risk appraisal of the individuals, and may give attention to fitness, stress management, smoking, cholesterol reduction, weight control, nutrition, cancer screening, and other matters on the basis of the risks detected. Synonym(s): wellness program.

health-related services: A term apparently used to include everything in the health care field except *medical care* (physician services).

health resources: Personnel (both professional and supportive), facilities, funds, and technology which are available or could be made available for health services.

Health Security Act (HSA): President Clinton's proposal for health care reform, which has been introduced in four bills. Three bills were introduced in the Senate:
S 1757, by Senator Mitchell ("Mitchell bill")
S 1775, by Senator Moynihan, tailored for referral to the Senate Finance Committee ("Moynihan bill")
S 1779, by Senator Kennedy, tailored for referral to the Senate Labor and Human Resources Committee ("Kennedy bill")
One bill was introduced in the House of Representatives:
HR 3600, by Representative Gephardt ("Gephardt bill").
References in this book to the *Health Security Act (HSA)* are to President Clinton's proposal as presented to Congress on October 27, 1993.

health security card (HSC): Under the *Health Security Act (HSA)*, an electronic card to be carried by the covered individual attesting to her/his participation in a given health care plan, and carrying, in addition, the individual's *unique identifier number (UIN)*, information on any supplementary insurance, and any other information specified by the *National Health Board (NHB)*. HSCs are to be issued by both regional health alliances and corporate health alliances (see *health alliance*). An HSC is a specialized type of *patient card*.

health service area: A specific geographic area considered in the governmental *health planning* process (see *planning*). The boundaries of health service areas were established in compliance with 1974 federal legislation on the basis of population, political subdivisions, geography, and other factors. The term "health service area" may also be used more loosely to mean service area, the area from which a facility or program actually draws its patients or clients, that is, its "catchment area."

health service network: Under *HR 3573*, a nonprofit private entity that (1) meets certain stated requirements as to services to be provided (or arranged for); (2) characteristics of the populations to be served; (3) requires provision of services regardless of ability to pay, (4) sets up requirements for participating providers; and (5) stipulates the governance.

health services: A term without specific definition which pertains to any services which are health-related.

health services research: Research pertaining to the *efficiency* and *effectiveness* of various organizational forms for health care delivery, administrative approaches, relationship to needs, and like matters.

Health Standards Board (HealSB): One of three advisory boards to the *National Health Board (NHB)* proposed by the *Jackson Hole Group*. The HealSB, if the proposal is implemented, will "assess medical technologies, medical practice effectiveness, and consumer opinions on health; advises on the list of effective services that will constitute the *Uniform Effective Health Benefits* [UEHB] set to be used as a national standard. Will consist of representative from insurance, employer, and consumer groups."

health system: A system designed to take responsibility for the *health* of its defined community; it involves "outreach" rather than "response" or "reaction." This is in contrast with with a health *care* system (see *health care system*).

health systems agency (HSA): A nonprofit organization or agency set up under federal law to perform health planning functions, develop a *health systems plan*, conduct *certificate of need (CON)* reviews, and review the use of certain federal funds.

health systems plan: A five-year plan prepared by a *health systems agency (HSA)*.

HEART: See *Health Equity and Access Reform Today Act of 1993*.

heroic treatment: See *extraordinary treatment* under *treatment*.

HHA: See *home health agency*.

HHS: A short abbreviation for the *Department of Health and Human Services (DHHS)*.

HI: Hospital Insurance Program. See *Medicare, Part A*, under *Medicare*.

"HICKFA" or "HICKVA": Common pronunciations of the acronym HCFA. See *Health Care Financing Administration*.

"HICK-PIX": "Acronym" sometimes used for "health insurance purchasing cooperative (HIPC)" or "health plan purchasing cooperative (HPPC)." See *health alliance (HA)*.

"HICKY": "Acronym" sometimes used for "health care quality improvement (HCQI)." See *quality improvement*.

HIP: Hospital Insurance Program. See *Medicare, Part A*, under *Medicare*. See also *health insurance plan*.

HIPC: Health insurance purchasing cooperative. See *health alliance (HA)*.

HIS: See *hospital information system* under *information system*.

HISB: See *Health Insurance Standards Board*.

HITF: See *Health Insurance Trust Fund*.

HMO: See *health maintenance organization*.

holistic health: See *wholistic health*.

home care: See *home health care*.

home care program: See *home health care program*.

home health agency (HHA): Essentially the same as a *home health care program* in that it provides medical and other health services in the patient's home. Unlike the home health care program, which provides services itself, the home health agency has the option of arranging the services by contracting with others. The term "home health agency" is applied to both nonprofit and proprietary bodies.

home health care: Care at the levels of skilled nursing care and intermediate care provided in the patient's home through an agency which has the resources necessary to provide that care. The care is given under the prescription of a physician by professional nurses and other health care professionals (social workers, physical therapists, and so forth), as appropriate. Services may also include homemaking and personal care services.
Home health care is a growing alternative to skilled nursing facilities and units (SNFs and SNUs) and to intermediate care facilities (ICFs) and units. Also called "in-home care" and "home care." See also *home life care*.

home health care program: An organization that provides medical and other health services in the patient's home. Synonym(s): home care program.

home life care: Supportive services provided by an agency in order to permit an individual who is able to carry out the activities of daily living (ADL) to remain at home rather than being placed in an institution. The services are given by homemakers and home aids rather than by nurses. One benefit of having such trained assistance in the home is that the worker going into the home is in a position to detect the need for and to obtain nursing services as required. Home life care is distinguished from home health care in that home health care includes nursing services under the direction of a physician rather than simply homemaking care. See also *home health care.*

hospice program: A program that assists with the physical, emotional, spiritual, psychological, social, financial, and legal needs of the dying patient and his or her family. The service may be provided in the patient's home or in an institution (or division of an institution) set up for the purpose. Volunteers are integral parts of the staff. Bereavement care for the family is also included. Hospice care and hospices are encouraged by Medicare. See also *comfort care.*

hospital-based professional: Under *HR 3080*, " . . . a health professional (including an allied health professional) who has expertise in providing one or more emergency medical services and who normally provides the services at a medical facility."

prehospital-based professional: Under *HR 3080*, " . . . a health professional (including an allied health professional) who has expertise in providing one or more emergency medical services and who normally provides the services at the site of the medical emergency or during transport to a medical facility."

hospital chain: See *multihospital system.*

hospital district: A special political subdivision created (by law in some states) solely to operate the hospital and other health care institutions.

hospital electronic medical data standards: Under *HR 3080*, the Secretary of Health and Human Services is to promulgate for hospitals 1) . . . "a definition of a standard set of data elements for use by utilization and quality control peer review organizations; 2) a definition of the set of comprehensive data elements [including 1) above]; 3) standards for an electronic patient care information system with data obtained at the point of care, including standards to protect against the unauthorized use and disclosure of information; 4) a specification of, and manner of presentation of, the individual data elements of the sets and system under this subsection; 5) standards concerning the transmission of electronic medical data; and (6 standards relating to confidentiality of patient-specific information." These standards will become mandatory for hospitals participating in Medicare and the Veterans Administration. " . . . a health benefit plan may not require . . . that a provider . . . provide any data element not in the set of comprehensive data elements specified . . . " The Secretary may also set similar standards for providers other than hospitals.

Hospital Health Plan (HHP): A specific model of *physician-hospital organization (PHO)* whose managed care plan is emerging as an alternative to the typical *health maintenance organization (HMO).* Sometimes called a "community health plan," it was developed by Richard Ya Deau, MD, in 1984. HHPs are established with the assistance of *Hospital Health Plan Corporation (HHPC)*. To use the title Hospital Health Plan (HHP), which is copyrighted by HHPC, a plan must have certain attributes:

(1) An HHP is designed to provide the services needed for its own defined population; it is "community rated" in benefits as well as in premium structure (see *community rating* under *rating*). Its health services are those required for prevention of disease, injury, and disability and for provision of optimal care, with the goal of achieving optimal health for the community rather than simply health care for those who present themselves. It is designed to manage care rather than manage dollars.

(2) An HHP can only be established after a thorough feasibility study and actuarial analysis which provides evidence that the proposed plan will (1) have an adequate enrollment; (2) have adequate participation by providers and others; (3) be able to offer its locally-defined benefit package for a saleable premium; (4) have a sound business and capitalization plan; and (5) be able to meet the state's requirements for licensure as an insurance company (reinsurance protects against unexpected loss). As a result of this careful preparation, several HHPs are in successful operation (including repaying their start-up financing) with as few as 12-15,000 enrollees.

(3) An HHP is a nonprofit insurance company, and since none of the premium income is committed to shareholders or equity investors, it is able to function with a "medical loss ratio" (portion of the premium spent on benefits) reported to be about 93%. In a nonprofit operation, the higher this ratio is, the better, since the plan exists to provide care. (In a for-profit insurance company, the incentive is to keep this number low (often as low as 75%) in order to reward the investors.) Thus the nonprofit plan can provide more care with a lower premium.

(4) Governance of an HHP is by a local board of directors which includes physicians, health care facilities, and enrollees.

(5) The physicians in the HHP develop the medical policies and oversee their implementation, rather than being overseen by an "outside" HMO.

(6) The hospital(s)' financial survival is insured by including in the financing of the HHP a capitation amount for the predicted hospitalizations for the enrolled population.

(7) Physicians may be paid by either fee-for-service or capitation, depending on the policies of the plan and individual preference.

The Hospital Health Plan model is also designed to meet the expected, forthcoming federal requirements to be certified as an *accountable health plan (AHP)*.

An HHP has available to it, under license from HHPC, computer software for individual case management and also an in-depth management information system. This software has been developed for and with a number of operating HHPs, and thus the development and maintenance costs are shared. Each HHP can tailor the software to its own particular needs.

Hospital Health Plan Corporation (HHPC): A corporation in Minnesota which assists communities, their hospitals, and their physicians in establishing *Hospital Health Plans (HHPs)*, and provides continuing assistance, case management support software, analytical software for managing the health plan, and liaison with other HHPs. Hospital Health Plan Corp., 4453 Lake Avenue South, Suite 201, White Bear Lake, MN 55110. Telephone 612-429-2298.

hospital information system (HIS): See *information system*.

Hospital Insurance Program (HI): See *Medicare, Part A*, under *Medicare*.

hospitalization: A period of stay in the hospital. Also, the placing of a patient in the hospital.

partial hospitalization: Treatment which involves the use of hospital day bed or night beds or *adult day care* (see *day care*) services on a regularly scheduled basis. The services provided may include medical, social, nutritional, psychological, and others.

HPA: See *Health Policy Agenda for the American People*.

HPPC: Health plan purchasing cooperative. See *health alliance (HA)*.

HPSB: See *Health Plan Standards Board*.

HR 3080: "Michel bill." This is the Republican health care reform bill, introduced in the House of Representatives by Representative Michel. Also known as the "Affordable Health Care Now Act of 1993."

HR 3222: "Cooper-Grandy bill." Also called "Managed Competition Act of 1993" (introduced in the Senate by the "Breaux bill," S 1759). Some call it the "Clinton Lite" health reform plan.

HR 3573: "Rowland bill." The health care reform bill introduced in the House of Representatives by Representative Rowland. It proposes demonstration projects involving community health authorities (CHA) (see *community health authority*). Also known as the "Community Health Improvement Act of 1993."

HR 3600: "Gephardt bill." See *Health Security Act (HSA)*.

HR 3704: "Thomas bill." Also called the "Health Equity and Access Reform Today Act of 1993 (HEART)." Introduced in the Senate as the "Chafee bill" (S 1770).

HRQOL: See *health-related quality of life* under *quality of life*.

HSA: See *health systems agency*.

I

IACCAPH: See *Interagency Advisory Committee on Competition, Anti-Trust Policy, and Health Care.*

IAD: See *instructional advance directive* under *advance directive.*

ICCS: See *International Classification of Clinical Services.*

ICD: See *International Classification of Diseases.*

ICD-9-CM: See *International Classification of Diseases, Ninth Revision, Clinical Modification.*

ICD-10: See *International Statistical Classification of Diseases and Related Health Problems.*

IDN: Integrated delivery network. See *integrated delivery system.*

IDS: See *integrated delivery system.*

IHCA: See *individual health care account.*

IMC: See *indigent medical care.*

IMIS: Integrated management information system. See *management information system (MIS)* under *information system.*

implicit: "Naturally" a part of, although not specifically stated. See *explicit* for further discussion.

in-home care: See *home health care.*

in-network: An adjective applied to a provider or a service when the provider is a part of the health care network (or system) or the service is available within the network, and thus the cost has been the subject of prior agreement. The antonym is, of course, "out-of-network."

incentive: A reward for desired behavior. In health care, this term is used in regard to rewards to institutions and individuals for decreasing hospital and physician costs, and for encouraging patients to be frugal in demands for health care. Sometimes incentives are negative, for example, when a patient is required to pay the first dollars for a service (this payment is called a deductible). The deductible is a "disincentive" to seek the care, and thus an incentive to be frugal. See also *copayment.*

incremental: An adjective which describes a process which proceeds step-by-step, and each step adds an increment (increase in quantity or value) to the step preceding. The term is being used with a different meaning in health care reform discussions to mean a process of change which happens bit-by-bit rather than all at once; action in contrast with an approach in which substantial health care reform steps would occur simultaneously.

A better word might be "additive." Various actions of reform, such as *cost controls* and *tort reform*, for example, taken incrementally would be taken separately. Changes made one at a time might be less traumatic, but would extend the whole reform process over a considerable time, all essential changes might never occur, and generally the end result is not likely to be as complete a change as might be desirable. Furthermore, the pieces, when finally in place, may not fit together well.

indemnity benefits or insurance: See *benefits*.

independent physician association (IPA): A type of health care provider organization composed of physicians, in which the physicians maintain their own practices but agree to furnish services to patients who have signed up for a *prepayment plan* in which the physician services are supplied by the IPA. An IPA is not a *health maintenance organization (HMO)*, a *health care organization (HCO)*, or a *preferred provider organization (PPO)*.

index rate: Under *HR 3080*, " . . . with respect to a class of business, the arithmetic average of the applicable base premium rate and the corresponding highest premium rate for the class."

indigent: A condition defined by the federal, state, or local government. Any individual whose income and other resources fall below the level defined is declared to be indigent. Note that "*medically indigent*" and "indigent" usually have different definitions.

medically indigent: The condition, as defined by the federal, state, or local government, of lacking the financial ability to pay for one's medical care. Any individual whose income and other resources falls below the defined level is declared to be medically indigent and may qualify for public assistance.

indigent medical care (IMC): Care for patients whose income falls below a level usually set by statute or regulation as defining indigency. Such care is provided without charge or for reduced charges, but the institution must find the resources by "overcharges" to other patients (or their payers), supplementary appropriations, public subscription, or elsewhere. See *cost-shifting*.

Indigo Institute: A *501(c)(3)* organization which conducts and disseminates research on the organization, function, and financing of health care. The Institute explores innovative ways of changing the present health care system and thus the behavior of those who provide and those who receive care, so that communities may deliver health care with quality, in an efficient manner, for all. Indigo Institute, 1700 K Street, Suite 906, Washington DC 20006-3817. Telephone 202-466-4341. See also *Blue Indigo*.

indirect medical education: Under the *Health Security Act (HSA)*, the activities in research, development of new medical technology, treatment of rare and unusually severe illnesses, and specialized patient care.

individual and small employer purchasing group (purchasing group): Under *HR 3704*, a nonprofit corporation which appears to be the equivalent of the *health alliance* called for by HSA.

individual health care account (IHCA): A proposed method of financing health care costs by giving tax advantages to individuals who establish and maintain personal "individual health care accounts (ICHAs)" similar in concept to individual retirement accounts (IRAs). Money placed in such accounts would be excluded from the individual's taxable income and would be invested, with principal and income to be used only for specified health care. ICHAs could be a replacement for financing by Medicare for the elderly, a supplement to Medicare, or both. Synonym(s): health IRA, medical IRA.

individual with disability: Under the *Health Security Act (HSA)*, (1) any individual requiring help with activities of daily living (ADL) for a specified period, (2) an individual with severe cognitive or mental impairment, (3) an individual with severe or profound mental retardation, and (4) a severely disabled child who would otherwise require hospital or other institutional care for more than a specified period.

industry screening: See *blacklisting*.

information system: A poorly defined term used to refer to anything from a pencil and paper to a full-blown computer system. Usually the term "information system" is modified by words specifying its purpose, such as "*management information system (MIS)*."

case mix management information system (case mix MIS): An information system which combines and correlates, on an individual patient basis, medical data abstracted from the hospital medical record of the patient (*discharge abstract*; see *abstract*) and from the patient's bill. Data analyses and displays relate *charges*, by *Diagnosis Related Groups* (DRGs), to receipts or allowances for those DRGs for the hospital and for individual physicians. A case mix MIS may be provided *in-house*, off-site, or through *shared services* (see *service (4)*). See also *case mix*.

Clinical Information System (CLICKS): A proprietary medical database system developed in Israel.

community health integrated management information system (CHIMIS): A set of computer systems and communication devices extending throughout the community in order to facilitate the exchange of clinical, financial, and management information among all parties involved: physicians, hospitals, schools, pharmacies, employers, and others involved in health and health care. The system provides continuous communication linkage among all the components of the entire health care system, so that the information for the care of patients is available where it is needed and when it is needed. Cost of care is reduced as is the cost of information management. The savings in both instances reflecting the minimizing of delays and the elimination of duplication in record-keeping.

Such a system is in operation in Milwaukee, and others are in various stages of development and testing. A CHIMIS is an extension throughout the community of the concept of the hospital's *integrated management information system (IMIS)*.

Computerized Patient Information System (CPIS): A computerized medical record system successfully installed in one ward of a psychiatric hospital in Israel in 1987, using the *Clinical Information System (CLICKS)* (see above).

hospital information system (HIS): A term applied to any system in a hospital dealing with information, usually with a computer involved. The kinds of data carried in the system will vary from hospital to hospital; there is no agreement yet on criteria which a system must meet to carry this title. An HIS is one kind of *management information system (MIS)*.

integrated management information system (IMIS): A management information system which includes in its scope (integrates into a single system) management information from all elements of an enterprise.

management information system (MIS): An essentially undefined term, applied to any system set up to provide information to or for management. There is no agreement on the kinds of information to be carried or the technology used. The term "MIS" often implies that a computer is involved--sometimes the hospital's computer system, sometimes *shared services* (see *service (4)*) with outside computers, and sometimes a *hospital discharge abstract system*. The *information* may include data on, for example, patients, finance, personnel, production, or the health care industry.

injury: Under *HR 3080*, " . . . any illness, disease, or other harm that is the subject of a medical malpractice liability action or a medical malpractice liability claim."

inpatient: A patient who receives care while being lodged in an institution.

inpatient care: Care rendered to patients who are lodged within a health care facility.

instructional advance directive (IAD): See *advance directive.*

insurance: A method of providing for money to pay for specific types of losses which may occur. Insurance is a contract (the insurance policy) between one party (the insured) and another (the insurer). The policy states what types of losses are covered, what amounts will be paid for each loss and for all losses, and under what conditions.

Two types of insurance commonly spoken of in health care are: (1) insurance covering the patient for health care services (health insurance, also called a "third-party-payer"); and (2) insurance covering the health care provider for risks associated with the delivery of health care (liability to a patient for malpractice, for example).

insurance claim form: The form on which a physician or other provider submits the claim for care given. Each insurance company may design and require its own form, as can the federal and state governments. One element of the *Health Security Act (HSA)* is to mandate that a single claim form be used by all insurors.

insurance clerk: See *reimbursement specialist (1).*

insurance coverage: Generally refers to the amount of protection available and the kind of loss which would be paid for under an *insurance* contract with an insurer. See also *benefits* and *coverage*.

insurance market reform program: See *State insurance market reform program.*

insurer: Under *HR 3080*, " . . . a licensed insurance company, a prepaid hospital or medical service plan, and a health maintenance organization offering such a plan to an employer . . . regulated under State law for solvency."

integrated delivery network (IDN): See *integrated delivery system.*

integrated delivery system (IDS): A nonspecific term for a variety of arrangements among health care providers in a specific area; apparently synonymous with "integrated delivery network (IDN)." The purpose of the IDS is to permit at least some degree of "one-stop shopping" for health care services, hospital, physician, and other. IDSs range in complexity from minimal formal agreements to a "fully integrated" organization which has insurance capability. No standard nomenclature has appeared for these arrangements; and there are an almost infinite variety of them. Arrangements include:

A. Independent physician associations (IPAs) in which physicians provide their services through the IPA to a given prepayment plan. This model has no direct integration of the physicians with the hospital. That link is provided by the prepayment plan.

B. Management service organizations (MSOs) in which the hospital provides a single point through which many physicians can have such tasks as their billings to various insurance companies and their scheduling handled. Only one staff needs to become expert in all the insurance policies; only one call can schedule consultations, referrals, hospitalizations.

C. Contracts between individual physicians and hospitals.

D. Hospitals employ the physicians.

E. Hospitals contract with physicians. The purchaser deals with the hospital. The hospital often pays the primary care physicians by capitation, and the specialists by fee-for-service.

F. Health maintenance organizations (HMOs) which contract with both physicians and hospitals, and which offer prepayment contracts.

G. "Foundations" in which the physicians and hospital(s) are members. The purchaser deals with the foundation, who may have a variety of arrangements with physicians and with hospitals.

H. "Health systems" in which all physicians are employed by the system, which also operates the hospital. Thus the purchaser can simply deal with the system.

I. "Care management organizations" which interpose a care manager between the patient and physician to administer the provision of services within the defined benefit package.

J. "Fully integrated" arrangements, which offer prepayment plans with defined benefit packages, i.e., they offer insurance packages to employers and other purchasers. Such plans typically manage the care as well. The philosophy of both the benefit package construction and the care management will vary from plan to plan.

integrated management information system (IMIS): See *management information system (MIS)* under *information system.*

integration: Integration is spoken of in health care today in terms of the linking together of components of the health care system:

horizontal integration: A linkage of hospitals (or other institutions and organizations) which are more or less alike, such as acute general hospitals, to form a *multihospital system.* The purpose of horizontal integration is to achieve economies of scale in operation, such as greater purchasing power and avoidance of duplication of facilities.

vertical integration: A linkage of hospitals (and other institutions and organizations) to form a system providing a range or continuum of care such as preventive, outpatient, acute hospital, long-term, home, and hospice care. The purpose of vertical integration is to keep the patient population within the one system for as many of its health care needs as possible.

integration of benefits: See *Commission on Integration of Health Benefits.*

intensivist: A physician who specializes in intensive care medicine.

Interagency Advisory Committee on Competition, Anti-Trust Policy, and Health Care (IACCAPH): Under *HR 3080,* an Advisory Committee composed of the Secretary of Health and Human Services HHS), the Attorney General, the Director of the Office of Management and Budget (OMB) (or their designees), and a representative of the Federal Trade Commission (FTC). The Advisory Committee will have duties to (1) study antitrust policy; (2) study and evaluate joint ventures receiving exemptions; and (3) advise Congress.

intermediary: See *fiscal intermediary.*

internal quality assurance: Under *HR 3704,* as it pertains to a risk contracting entity, such an entity must have " . . . in effect a written internal quality assurance program which includes a systematic process to achieve specified and measurable goals and objectives for access to, and quality of care, which . . . [the Act then spells out in great detail the attributes of the required plan]."

internal quality assurance program: Under *HR 3080,* pertains to both risk contracting entities and primary care case management entities. The program must be written and the entity must meet a detailed series of performance requirements. The program must be reviewed periodically by the State, and shall be subject to an "annual external independent review" provided by the State.

International Classification of Clinical Services (ICCS): A *classification (1)* and *coding* system developed by the *Commission on Professional and Hospital*

Activities (CPHA) for certain hospital-provided services in order to standardize patient care data and to facilitate computer handling of those data. Schemas are available for laboratory services, diagnostic imaging, and drugs. Similar schemas are under development for supplies, anesthesia, cardiology, respiratory therapy, physical medicine, nursing, and other categories.

International Classification of Diseases (ICD): A publication of the World Health Organization (WHO), revised periodically. The edition now in use is the 9th Revision, dated 1975. The full title is *The International Classification of Diseases, Injuries, and Causes of Death.* This classification, which originated for use in classifying deaths, is used world-wide for that purpose. In addition, it has been used widely in the U.S. for hospital diagnosis classification since about 1955 through adaptations and modifications made in the U.S. of the 7th, 8th, and 9th Revisions. Modification was required for hospital use since, as discussed under *classification (1)*, the purpose of the classification determines the pigeonholes; for example, "death pigeonholes" are quite different, in many instances, from those for illnesses and injuries. The modification in current use, the *International Classification of Diseases, Ninth Revision, Clinical Modification (ICD-9-CM)*, published in 1978, has been in official use in the U.S. since 1979.

The 10th Revision, being released currently, contains additional reasons why people seek help from, and how they are affected by, both the public health programs and the health care systems of the world. See *International Statistical Classification of Diseases and Related Health Problems (ICD-10).*

International Classification of Diseases, Ninth Revision, Clinical Modification (ICD-9-CM): The *classification (1)* in current use for *coding* of diagnoses and operations for indexing medical records by diagnoses and operations, for compiling hospital statistics, and for submitting bills in the *prospective payment system (PPS)*. ICD-9-CM is published by the *Commission on Professional and Hospital Activities (CPHA)* and by the federal government. *Annotated ICD-9-CM*, published by CPHA, is a version color-coded to alert users to reimbursement-related issues. See also *International Classification of Diseases (ICD)* and *International Statistical Classification of Diseases and Related Health Problems (ICD-10).*

International Statistical Classification of Diseases and Related Health Problems (ICD-10): The 10th Revision of the *International Classification of Diseases*, published by the World Health Organization (WHO). Volume 1, the Tabular List, has just been published, but the Alphabetic Index has not yet been released.

The original volume, published in 1900, was called *The International List of Causes of Death*. Subsequent revisions, about every ten years, have broadened the scope of the volume to include causes of injury and illness, their external causes, and "other factors influencing health status and contact with health services." The name was changed with the 7th Revision (1955) to *The International Classification of Diseases, Injuries, and Causes of Death.* This title was used for the 8th and 9th Revisions as well. With the 10th Revision, the title shown above has been adopted. In view of the

CH.	ICD-9	ICD-10	ICD-9 Chapter Title	ICD-10 Chapter Title

ICD-9 *vs* ICD-10: Comparison of Chapters, Codes, and Titles

CH.	ICD-9	ICD-10	*ICD-9 Chapter Title*	*ICD-10 Chapter Title*
I	001-139	A00-B99	Infectious and Parasitic Diseases	Certain Infectious and Parasitic Diseases
II	140-239	C00-D49	Neoplasms	Neoplasms
III	240-279		Endocrine, Nutritional and Metabolic Diseases and Immunity Disorders	
		D50-D99		Diseases of Blood and Blood-forming Organs and Certain Disorders Involving the Immune Mechanism
IV	280-289		Diseases of Blood and Blood-forming Organs	
		E00-E99		Endocrine, Nutritional and Metabolic Diseases
V	290-319	F00-F99	Mental Disorders	Mental and Behavioral Disorders
VI	320-389	G00-G99	Diseases of the Nervous System and Sense Organs	Diseases of the Nervous System
VII	390-459		Diseases of the Circulatory System	
		H00-H59		Diseases of the Eye and Adnexa
VIII	460-519		Diseases of the Respiratory System	
		H60-H99		Diseases of the Ear and Mastoid Process
IX	520-579		Diseases of the Digestive System	
		I00-I99		Diseases of the Circulatory System
X	580-629		Diseases of the Genitourinary System	
		J00-J99		Diseases of the Respiratory System
XI	630-676		Complications of Pregnancy, Childbirth, and the Puerperium	
		K00-K99		Diseases of the Digestive System

CH.	ICD-9	ICD-10	ICD-9 Chapter Title	ICD-10 Chapter Title
XII	680-709	L00-L99	Diseases of the Skin and Subcutaneous Tissue	Diseases of the Skin and Subcutaneous Tissue
XIII	710-739	M00-M99	Diseases of the Musculoskeletal System and Connective Tissue	Diseases of the Musculoskeletal System and Connective Tissue
XIV	740-759		Congenital Anomalies	
		N00-N99		Diseases of the Genitourinary System
XV	760-779		Certain Conditions Originating in the Perinatal Period	
		O00-O99		Pregnancy, Childbirth and Puerperium
XVI	780-799		Symptoms, Signs and Ill-Defined Conditions	
		P00-P99		Certain Conditions Originating in the Perinatal Period
XVII	800-999		Injury and Poisoning	
		Q00-Q99		Congenital Malformations, Deformations, and Chromosomal Abnormalities
XVIII		R00-R99		Symptoms, Signs, and Abnormal Clinical and Laboratory Findings Not Elsewhere Classified
XIX		S00-T99		Injury, Poisoning and Certain Other Consequences of External Causes
XX		V01-Y99		External Causes of Morbidity and Mortality
XXI		Z00-Z99		Factors Influencing Health Status and Contact with Health Services
	E800-E999		Supplementary Classification of External Causes of Injury and Poisoning	

widespread use of *ICD-9* in the U.S., it is likely that the 10th Revision will be referred to as "*ICD-10*," despite the fact that this short title no longer reflects the actual title of the classification.

Major changes from the 9th Revision include the adoption of alphanumeric codes (previously most of the codes were numeric), the provision of categories for additional "other factors" (see *problem*), changes in the details of categories throughout the classification, changes in the chapters and chapter headings, and the inclusion of the previous "supplementary classifications" as chapters within the classification itself. A comparison between *ICD-9* and *ICD-10* is shown in the table on pages 76-77.

Interstudy: A nonprofit health care research body, a "think tank," based in Minneapolis, Minnesota. See also *Jackson Hole Group*.

intervention: See *therapeutic intervention*.

IPA: See *independent physician association*.

J

Jackson Hole Group: An informal "think tank" founded by Paul Elwood, MD, President of *Interstudy*, in the early 1970s. Elwood convenes a small group of persons interested in the problems they perceive in the health care system at his home in Jackson Hole, Wyoming, and leads informal discussions on possible solutions to the problems. Their commitment is "to shaping sensible, market-based health care reform in the U.S." A total of nearly 90 individuals have participated in the discussions, now held about every three months, although any given meeting is limited to about twenty invited persons. The three constant members are Elwood, Alain Enthoven, Stanford University health economist, and Lynn Etheredge, Washington, DC, based consultant. The group gained national attention with the 1991 release of a "white paper" entitled "The 21st Century American Health System: The Jackson Hole Group Proposals for Health Care Reform Through Managed Competition." The group may be reached at P.O. Box 350, Teton Village, WY 83025-7000. Telephone 307-0739-1176; FAX 307-739-1177.

JCAHO: See *Joint Commission on Accreditation of Healthcare Organizations*.

JCAHO standard: See *standard*.

job lock: Remaining in employment for fear of losing one's health insurance coverage. This is caused by waiting periods for pre-existing conditions, high rates, and outright denials of coverage.

Joint Commission on Accreditation of Healthcare Organizations (JCAHO): An independent, nonprofit, voluntary organization sponsored by the American College of Physicians (ACP), the American College of Surgeons (ACS), the American Hospital Association (AHA), the American Medical

Association (AMA), and other medical, dental, and health care organizations. JCAHO develops *standards* and provides accreditation surveys and certification to hospitals and to other health care organizations, such as psychiatric facilities, long-term care facilities, ambulatory care, and hospital care. It also offers education programs, consultation, and publications.

joint venture: A business arrangement between two or more parties to share profits, losses, and control. In health care, the term often indicates a formalized cooperative effort between the hospital and its *medical staff* (or physicians from its medical staff), as opposed to a relationship in which the two, hospital and physicians, are in competition with one another. For example, a joint venture may be established in order to set up a diagnostic facility.

The legal form of the joint venture may be a *partnership* (general or limited), lease arrangement, *corporation*, or other form suited to the requirements of the venture. Sometimes the term "joint venture" is used synonomously with "partnership"; however, while a partnership may be a joint venture, not all joint ventures are partnerships. "Joint venture" may also have a specific legal meaning under state law.

health care joint venture: Under *HR 3080*, provision is made for granting exemption from liability under antitrust laws for joint ventures in health care which meet the requirements of the Act.

integrated joint venture: A joint venture arrangement to provide prepaid health services in which providers who would otherwise be competitors pool their capital to finance the venture by themselves, or together with others, and share substantial risk of adverse financial results caused by unexpectedly high utilization or costs of health care services.

K

Kaiser-Permanente: Used to refer to one or more parts of the Kaiser-Permanente Medical Care Program, America's largest private health care system, and considered to be a pioneer in comprehensive prepayment systems. It includes the following three components:

(1) Kaiser Foundation Health Plan, the *health maintenance organization (HMO)* under which the members are organized. In July 1993, Kaiser HMOs based in San Francisco and Los Angeles, each with over 2 million members, were top ranked by *Money* magazine. The San Francisco HMO was started in 1945.

(2) Kaiser Foundation Hospitals, a nonprofit corporation that provides the hospital services to the HMO members. According to the American Hospital Association's *Guide to the Health Care Field*, this component had 30 hospitals (6,454 beds) in 1992, in California, Hawaii, Ohio, and Oregon.

(3) The Permanente Medical Groups, the physician partnerships and

professional corporations which provide the actual medical services to the HMO.

Kennedy bill (S 1779):   See *Health Security Act (HSA)*.

L

large employer: Under *HR 3704*, " . . . an employer that is not a small employer." (See *small employer*.)

large employer health plan: Under *HR 3704*, a health care plan for employers with 101 or more employees. Certain standards for such plans are to be promulgated by the Secretary [of Health and Human Services], certain others by the Secretary of Labor. Both Secretaries are to take into account standards established by the National Association of Insurance Commissioners (NAIC). Every large employers must offer " . . . at least 1) a qualified large employer plan that includes the standard package, and 2) a qualified large employer plan that includes the catastrophic package."

legacy system: A computer term referring to an inherited set of independent computer systems within an organization (enterprise). The term comes into use as enterprises seek to consolidate the systems of the past into a single information source, either by somehow linking them together so that they can communicate with each other (and with the inquirer) or, more likely, by replacing them with an *integrated management information system (IMIS)* (see *information system*). Hospitals commonly have installed at different times independent computer systems for laboratory, X-ray, business office, and admitting, for example. Unless this legacy system is replaced by an IMIS, (1) it is impossible to obtain a comprehensive view of the hospital's activities, (2) since much of the same information is found in each system, such as patient demographic data, there is a much higher likelihood of error than if there were a single entry for each piece of information, and (3) there is duplication of cost.

length of stay (LOS): The number of days between a patient's *admission* and *discharge*. The day of admission is counted as a day, while the day of discharge is not. This abbreviation is often misused when the intent is to refer to *average length of stay (ALOS)*.

average length of stay (ALOS): A standard hospital statistic. For a given group of patients, their total lengths of stay are added together, and that total is divided by the total number of patients in the group. For a "hospital ALOS," the formula adds together the LOSs of all patients discharged from the hospital (for their entire stays) in a given time period, and divides that sum by the number of patients discharged in that same time period. ALOS is often incorrectly referred to as "LOS"; however, LOS means "length of stay" and pertains to an individual patient.

The ALOS may be calculated not only for the entire hospital, but also for specific age groups or *diagnosis related groups* (DRGs), for example. It may also be calculated in a more refined ("normalized") manner by making an adjustment for the *case mix* of the hospital. An ALOS which adjusts for the age distribution of the patients, for example, makes for fairer comparisons between hospitals than one without such an adjustment; adjusting for additional factors, such as the distribution of patients among DRGs, further improves the statistic for interhospital comparison purposes.

level of care: The amount (intensity) and kind of professional nursing care required for a patient in order to achieve the desired medical and nursing care objectives for the patient, that is, to carry out the orders of the attending physician and to meet the patient's nursing care needs. The term "level of care" applies primarily to care provided outside the acute hospital. Three levels of care are recognized: skilled nursing care (the highest level), intermediate care, and rest home care (custodial care, the lowest level).

Levels of care (and facilities to provide them) have specific definitions in Medicare, Medicaid, and other payment programs, and also under statutes and regulations of the various states. The determination of the level of care to be provided to a given patient is a serious matter; on the one hand, the patient should be placed at the lowest level of care commensurate with the patient's needs as a matter both of appropriate care and of economy, while, on the other hand, payment is greater for each succeedingly higher level of care.

liability (1): Responsibility to do something, pay something, or refrain from doing something. Liability is used to refer to a legal obligation, often one which must be enforced by a lawsuit.

corporate liability: Legal responsibility of a corporation, rather than of an individual. In the health care context, the term is often used to denote a specific type of responsibility: that of the hospital as an institution (corporation) to exercise reasonable care in selecting, retaining, and granting *privileges* to members of its *medical staff*. A hospital may be liable to a patient injured by a physician (or other health professional) if the hospital knew or should have known that the physician was not competent to perform the procedure involved (or to otherwise treat the patient), and did not reasonably act to protect the patient (for example, by restricting that physician's privileges or by requiring supervision). "Knew" means that the hospital may not "look the other way" if it learns of problems with a physician which could endanger patients; "should have known" means that the hospital must diligently investigate a physician's credentials prior to granting staff privileges, *and* that the hospital must systematically monitor the care provided by that physician, once on the staff. See also *privileges* and *credentialing*.

enterprise liability: Same as *organizational liability* (see below).

joint and several liability: The responsibility of more than one *defendant* to share in legal liability to a *plaintiff*. If the defendants (for example, the hospital and a physician) are jointly and severally liable, each is responsible to pay the entire judgment to the plaintiff (although the plaintiff cannot collect more than the amount of the judgment).

organizational liability: A system under which individual health care providers are relieved of liability for medical malpractice, and health care organizations such as hospitals and health maintenance organizations bear liability for malpractice committed by their affiliated care providers, whether or not those providers are employees of the organization. The system is proposed by Kenneth S. Abraham, JD, Class of 1962 Professor of Law, University of Virginia School of Law. Probably being renamed "enterprise liability."

product liability: An area of law which imposes legal responsibility on manufacturers (and in some cases distributors and retailers) of goods which leave the factory in an unreasonably dangerous condition, and which in fact cause harm to someone because of that condition. Product liability does not require proof that the manufacturer was negligent (careless) in designing or producing the item (see *negligence*).

professional liability: A legal obligation which is the result of performing (or failing to perform) something which one does (or should have done) as a professional. A physician who drives carelessly and injures another will be simply "liable" for that person's injuries; the fact that she is a physician is not relevant to the fact that she injured the other person. If that same physician carelessly misses a diagnosis and again injures another, the legal responsibility is called "professional liability," since her actions as a physician caused the injury. Sometimes the phrase "professional liability" is used interchangeably with "professional *negligence*," but that usage is inaccurate because a professional can become liable for reasons other than negligence (for example, by improperly disclosing a patient's confidences, operating without *informed consent*, or abandoning a patient).

strict liability: Legal responsibility for injury which is imposed regardless of any fault, or lack of fault. A plaintiff suing under strict liability does not need to show that the defendant was negligent, reckless, or malicious. The plaintiff does, however, still need to prove the existence of a defect (such as in a product) or an action (such as selling liquor to an intoxicated person) and that the defect or action caused the plaintiff's injuries.

liability (2): In finance, an obligation to pay. Liabilities are shown on an institution's *balance sheet* under such headings as "accounts payable" (money owed to vendors and others), "accrued salaries" (when a statement is drawn before checks have been issued for a given pay period), and the like.

current liability: A liability due within one year.

life care: A *long-term care* arrangement ("*alternative*") in which all care required for the lifetime of the participant is provided. A retirement home which agrees to provide not only facilities for independent living, but also nursing care and hospitalization to residents as needed, is a "life care community."

lifetime reserve: A Medicare term referring to the pool of 60 days of hospital care upon which a patient may draw after he or she has used up the maximum Medicare benefit for a single *spell of illness*.

living will: See *advance directive.*

lobbying: Attempts to influence the passage or defeat of legislation. There are limits on such activities, and certain other political activities, by *tax-exempt* organizations, such as *501(c)(3) corporations.* Hospitals are often tax-exempt 501(c)(3) organizations, and thus are limited in their lobbying (and campaigning) efforts.

local health department: A unit of local government which is the action arm of national and state *public health* agencies. It typically carries out some clinical services, environmental services, and support services. Clinical services may include, for example, dental health, occupational health, nursing, maternal and child health, family planning, communicable disease, and *Women, Infants and Children's Programs* (WIC). Environmental services may include general environment, *vector* control, animal control, and pollution control. Support services may include, in addition to administration, vital statistics, laboratory, and health education.

long-term care (LTC): Care for patients, regardless of age, who have chronic diseases or disabilities, and who require preventive, diagnostic, therapeutic, and supportive services over long periods of time. LTC may call on a variety of health care professionals (such as physicians, nurses, physical therapists, and social workers) as well as non-professionals (family, others) and may be delivered in a health care or other institution or in the home.

Long-term care customarily refers to those for whom the care is thought to be necessary for the rest of their lives, i.e., for whom the disability is thought not to be reversible. When the prediction is that the person can be returned to a more independent mode of living, the person is placed under skilled nursing or intermediate care (under "extended care" rather than "long-term care"). Rehabilitation efforts are, however, made for persons in long-term care, and some of them do recover sufficiently to become less dependent.

Some of the proposed health care reform bills include definitions of long-term care. Under *HR 3080,* it is defined as " ... diagnostic, preventive, therapeutic, rehabilitative, maintenance, or personal care ... for a chronically ill individual ... provided in a setting other than an acute care hospital ... pursuant to a continuing plan of care prescribed by a physician or registered professional nurse. Such term does not include food or lodging provided in an institutional or other setting, or basic living services associated with the maintenance of a household or participation in community life ... " *HR 3704* has a similar definition.

LOS: See *length of stay.*

loss ratio: Total incurred claims for a given insurance plan divided by the total premiums.

LTC: See *long-term care.*

M

MAAC: See *maximum allowable actual charges.*

macro measures: In health care, refers to steps taken to improve the health care system at the community level (for example, local, state, or national) with respect to such problems as insurance, financing, tort reform, access, and the like, rather than care to individual patients. See also *micro measures.*

macroeconomics: The economic theory which pertains to forces which determine the decisions and actions of populations, rather than of individuals. The latter theory is called microeconomics.

MADPA: See *Medicaid Antidiscriminatory Drug Pricing and Patient Benefit Restoration Act.*

magnetic sitter: An electronic system similar to that used in clothing stores to detect removal of a magnetically "marked" garment past a sensor at the exit. Similar magnetic "sitters" are used to keep track of patients who, because of confusion, may wander away or enter a dangerous area. Such patients, who would otherwise have to be restrained, may be granted freedom of movement, with assurance that sensors placed near exits, windows, and other areas denied to patients will inform the nursing staff.

magnetized health benefit cards: See *Medicare and Medicaid magnetized health benefit cards.*

major diagnostic category (MDC): A term used in the *prospective payment system (PPS).* All patients are ultimately classified into one of the 468 *diagnosis related group*s (DRGs) (categories). On the way to that classification, each patient first falls into one of 23 MDCs on the basis of the patient's principal diagnosis; the patient is then further classified according to age, complications, whether an operating room procedure was performed, and so forth.

major medical insurance: Health insurance to cover a *catastrophic illness.*

malpractice: A failure of care or skill by a professional, which causes loss or injury and results in legal *liability (1).* This narrow definition means the same as *professional negligence* (see *negligence*). Some use the term "malpractice" more broadly to describe all acts by a health care professional in the course of providing health care--including breach of contract--which may result in legal liability. Malpractice suits--and resultant insurance and other costs--have become a large problem in the health care system. See *tort reform.*

malpractice reform: See *tort reform.*

managed care: Any arrangement for health care in which someone is interposed between the patient and physician and has authority to place restraints on how and from whom the patient may obtain medical and health services, and what services are to be provided in a given situation. Under the terms of a *prepaid health plan*, for example, the payer may require: that except in an emergency, a designated person (a *patient care manager (PCM)* or "gatekeeper") be the patient's first contact with the health care services; that all care be authorized and coordinated by the gatekeeper rather than permitting the patient to go directly to specialists; that only certain physicians and facilities be used (if the prepayment plan is to pay for the services); that *preadmission certification (PAC)* precede hospitalization; that second opinions be obtained for *elective* surgery; and that certain care be delivered in the outpatient setting. Although the primary stimulus for introducing managed care was to attempt to keep costs down, there is increasing interest in trying to see that each patient gets the care indicated and is spared unnecessary or ill-advised care. See *Hospital Health Plan*. Synonym(s): collaborative care, coordinated care.

managed care firm: A term applied to a variety of organizations which contract to provide management services for the reduction and control of health care costs to corporations, insurers, and *third party administrators*. Managed care firms employ such methods as making decisions as to what care is to be given individual patients and where it will be provided, negotiating contracts with providers as to quantities of and prices (often discounts) for services, and auditing and approving the bills for the services the patients receive. Sometimes the managed care firm offers a stipulated care package for a prearranged *capitation* fee. Typically such firms do not themselves provide care and do not operate hospitals or other health care facilities. Managed care firms often contend that they can reduce the costs of health care for a client by 25 percent or more.

managed care plan: An organization providing *managed care*, a method of arranging for health care to achieve certain goals: (1) to benefit the individuals served by the plan and, at the same time, (2) to benefit the population being served, and (3) to provide services in the most efficient, effective, and economic manner in view of the finite resources available. A managed care plan has a defined group of providers and an identified group of enrollees to be served. Forward-looking plans develop explicit standards of care to be required of their providers, and are concerned not only with treatment and amelioration of disease, but also with prevention. The plan may or may not operate its own hospitals or other health care facilities. Payment to the providers is typically prearranged by *capitation*. See, for example, *Hospital Health Plan*.

managed competition (MC): A strategy for purchasing health care in a manner which will obtain maximum value for the price for the purchasers of the health care and the recipients. The concept has been developed primarily by Alain Enthoven (Stanford University), and has been promulgated by the *Jackson Hole Group*.

The strategy depends on the existence of "sponsors" and acceptable providers, under government regulation. Sponsors for certain groups already exist in the form of large employers, state governments, and similar institutions. For smaller and less well-organized groups, an organization called a *health alliance (HA)* is envisioned as the sponsor. The HA is to be a nonprofit corporation established by appropriate employer and community groups. The sponsor acts as an intermediary between the population to be insured and the competing provider groups (*accountable health plans* (AHPs)) which take care of both financing and delivery of care. (For competition to occur, of course, there must be more than one supplier.)

The "competition" is price competition among annual premiums for a defined, standardized benefit package rather than for individual services. The competition is to be "informed" in that the sponsor has data and expertise to guide it, along with an informed, critical population of subscribers being served. Presumably the AHP which convinces both the sponsor and the consumers that it provides the highest quality of care, at the lowest cost for that quality, and with the most satisfied patients (beneficiaries), will flourish because of increased business.

The sponsor (1) selects participating AHPs, (2) makes sure that the eligible providers (AHPs) cannot evade price competition, (3) takes care of the enrollment process, (4) insists on equity, which includes such considerations as availability of the plan to every applicant (even though subsidy may be required), continuous coverage, community rating, and no exclusion for preexisting conditions, (5) makes sure that the premium is adjusted on the basis of the risks presented by the covered population so that surcharges or subsidies, as may be required, are applied and result in equal premiums among the AHPs, and (6) makes sure that the demand is *price-elastic* (that is, that the more subscribers, the lower the cost).

Managed competition proponents make the following contentions: (1) MC is expected to work because it depends on the application of proven microeconomic principles; (2) pluralism is insured because of the existence of a choice of providers; (3) individuals are made responsible for their own health; (4) all citizens are covered (although financing is not a component of the MC process).

Proponents insist that managed competition is *not*: free market, a voucher system, deregulation, more of the present system, mandatory enrollment in HMOs or large clinics, lower quality care, a blind experiment, a "buzz-word" without definition, a panacea, or a process difficult to implement, requiring a long time to put in place.

The concept was developed by Alain Enthoven, who has published widely on the subject (see, e.g., Enthoven, A. "Managed Competition: An Agenda for Action," *Health Affairs*, Vol. 7, No. 3, Summer 1988).

Managed Competition Act of 1993 (HR 3222 & S 1579): The health care reform bill introduced in the House of Representatives by Representatives Cooper and Grandy (HR 3222). Its companion bill in the Senate was introduced by Senator Breaux (S 1579). Also known as the "Cooper-Grandy bill."

mandate: To require or a requirement. In health care reform, the term is being used to refer to federal or state-imposed requirements on insurance companies, employers, and so forth, to pay for health care or provide specific benefits:

employer mandate: An approach to health care reform which would require employers to provide coverage for their employees or be penalized. Typically, employer mandate proposals are limited to employers with more than a stated number of full-time employees, say 25 or 50. Also called "play or else."

   play or pay: A slang phrase describing the option given to employers under some legislative proposals which require that the employer participate in the health care plan offered or pay for an acceptable alternative; usually means paying a tax, which would go to a public plan to provide for the employed uninsured and the unemployed. Synonym(s): "pay or play."

state mandate: State laws which mandate private health care insurers to cover a wide variety of services, including well baby care and so forth, sometimes resulting in premiums out of reach of small employers. See also *bare-bones health plan*.

mandatory assignment: A requirement for physicians to accept Medicare reimbursement as payment in full for their services; they would not be allowed to bill the patient for any difference between their fees and the amount that Medicare will pay (see *balance billing*).

market-based approach: See *consumer choice*.

market-driven system: See *economic system*.

market forces: The economic forces of supply and demand.

maternal and child health program (MCH program): A program providing preventive and treatment services for pregnant women, mothers, and children. The services may include health education (often with particular attention to nutrition) and family planning. Funding may be from federal, state, or local sources. One source of funds has been the U.S. Maternal and Child Health Program under the Social Security Act.

maximum allowable actual charges (MAAC): Limits for physician charge increases which were set by federal statute enacted in 1986. The statute applies only to physicians who are "non-participating" (that is, who have not agreed to accept the Medicare payment allowance as full payment). The limits apply to average charges, rather than charges for specific services; thus, compliance must be evaluated retrospectively, and enforcement is complicated.

MC: See *managed competition*.

McCarran-Ferguson Act: A 1945 act which declared that the insurance industry was not affected by federal laws regulating interstate commerce, unless the laws specifically applied to insurance. As a result, health care insurers have not been subject to federal antitrust laws. The *Health Security Act (HSA)* provides that the antitrust exemption for health care insurers would be repealed six months after enactment of the HSA.

MCH program: See *maternal and child health program*.

MDC: See *major diagnostic category*.

MedAccess plan: Under *HR 3080*, " . . . a health insurance plan (whether a managed care plan, indemnity plan, or other plan) that meets the following requirements: . . . A) (i) is designed to provide standard coverage . . . with substantial cost-sharing; (ii) is designed to provide only catastrophic coverage . . . or (iii) is designed to provide medisave coverage . . . (B) . . . includes only essential and medically necessary services, including medical, surgical, hospital, and preventive services; except that no specific procedure or treatment, or classes, thereof, is required to be covered in such a plan, by this Act or through regulations . . . " and meets certain other requirements as to guaranteed issue and consumer protection. Standards for the various levels of MedAccess plans are to be developed by the National Association of Insurance Commissioners (NAIC).

MedAccess catastrophic plan: Under *HR 3080*, " . . . a health insurance plan (whether a managed care plan, indemnity plan, or other plan) that meets the following requirements: . . . (A) . . . (ii) is designed to provide only catastrophic coverage . . . "if (A) benefits are available under the plan for a year only to the extent that expenses for covered services in a year exceed a deductible amount that is consistent with the requirement for a catastrophic health plan under [IRS code], and (B) the benefits are determined, in accordance with the set of actual equivalence rules . . . "

MedAccess medisave plan: Under *HR 3080*, " . . . a health insurance plan (whether a managed care plan, indemnity plan, or other plan) that meets the following requirements: . . . is (A) a catastrophic health plan [IRS requirements], and (B) a medical savings account [IRS requirements]."

MedAccess standard plan: Under *HR 3080*, " . . . a health insurance plan (whether a managed care plan, indemnity plan, or other plan) that meets the following requirements: . . . A) (i) is designed to provide standard coverage . . . with substantial cost-sharing; . . . "Standard coverage" is defined as "equal to the average actuarial value of a representative range of the different types of health benefits provisions (which include cost-sharing) typically offered as standard coverage in the small employer health coverage market . . . "

Medi-Cal: *Medicaid* in California. Since each state administers Medicaid, the program in California is unique (as are the programs in the other states).

Medicaid: The federal program which provides health care to *indigent* and *medically indigent* persons. While partially federally funded, the Medicaid program is administered by the states, in contrast with Medicare, which is federally funded and administered at the federal level. The Medicaid program was established in 1965 by amendment to the Social Security Act, under a provision entitled "Title XIX--Medical Assistance." Requirements for eligibility for Medicaid are set by each state as are, within certain limits, the benefits. For example, incomes above which persons are too affluent to qualify as eligible vary greatly from state to state, and "access" thus differs accordingly. (Medicare, on the other hand, provides like benefits from state to state.)

Medicaid Antidiscriminatory Drug Pricing and Patient Benefit Restoration Act (MADPA): A federal law enacted in 1990 which is aimed at pharmaceutical cost containment. It requires drug companies to provide, through a rebate system, the "best prices" in the Medicaid outpatient pharmacy program; established a moratorium on reductions in pharmacy service reimbursement rates; guarantees Medicaid outpatients access to drug therapy consultations with their pharmacists; and requires review, in the outpatient program, of drug therapy before each prescription is dispensed.

Medicaid buy-in: A health care reform approach which would permit uninsured individuals to enroll in Medicaid by paying premiums on a sliding scale.

medical care: Traditionally, care which was under the direction of a physician. More recently, "medical care" has also come to refer only to those portions of the care provided directly or personally by a physician, with the care given by other professionals (such as nursing care, rehabilitation, and the like) excluded, or at least semi-independent, from the definition. For example, "evaluation of medical care" has been replaced in most usage by "evaluation of patient care"; the latter term not only focuses on the patient, but also ensures that all components of the care--not just what the physician does--are included.

Health care reform generally includes a much broader range of concerns than medical care alone; in fact it is increasingly referred to as "health reform," perhaps to emphasize this fact.

Medical care will have specific definitions in legislation. For example, under *HR 1743*, it includes some transportation and housing incident to medical care.

medical care evaluation: The evaluation of the quality of medical care. Usually refers to the patient care audit (medical audit), which is a retrospective review of the quality of care of a group of patients, ordinarily a group with the same diagnosis or therapy.

medical condition: Under *HR 3222*, "a disease, illness, injury, or biological or psychological condition or status for which treatment is indicated to improve, maintain, or stabilize a health outcome, or which, in the absence of treatment, could lead to an adverse change in health outcome."

Medical Directive, The: See *advance directive.*

medical education, indirect: See *indirect medical education.*

medical indigence: The condition of being *medically indigent.* See *indigent.*

Medical Injury Compensation Reform Act (MICRA): A California statute enacted in the mid-1970s which is often proposed as a prototype for malpractice reform. Significant restrictions are placed on the rights of injured persons.

medical IRA: See *individual health care account.*

medical product: Under *HR 3080,* " . . . with respect to the allegation of a claimant, a drug [defined] or a medical device [defined] . . . "

medical review agency: An *agency* established under the *prospective payment system (PPS)* to carry out certain surveillance functions with respect to hospital and physician performance and detection of fraud.

medical safety promotion: Under *HR 3080,* research is to be carried out on (1) the prevention of and compensation for injuries resulting from professional and provider malpractice, and (2) outcomes of health care procedures. Furthermore, grants are to be available to States, local governments, nonprofit organizations, and health professional schools for " . . . A) educating the general public about the appropriate use of health care and realistic expectations of medical interventions; B) educating the public about the resources and role of health care professional licensing and disciplinary boards in investigating claims of incompetence or health care malpractice; and C) developing programs of faculty training and curricula for educating health care professionals in quality assurance, risk management, and medical injury prevention.

medical savings account: An account, similar in nature to an individual retirement account (IRA), allowed in several of the health care reform proposals: *HR 3080* includes a section which would amend the Internal Revenue Code of 1986 (relating to additional itemized deductions for individuals) so that " . . . there shall be allowed as a deduction the applicable percentage of the amounts paid in cash during the taxable year by or on behalf of such individual to a medical savings account for the benefit of such individual and . . . " spouse and dependents. This medical savings account must be " . . . a trust created or organized in the United States exclusively for the purpose of paying the medical expenses of the beneficiaries of such trust . . . " and it must meet defined requirements. "Medical expenses" may include both "medical care" and long-term care. Such accounts are also provided for under *HR 3704.*

medical self-regulatory entity: Under *HR-3080,* "a medical society or association, a specialty board, a recognized accrediting agency, or a hospital medical staff." which may be granted antitrust exemption for its *standard setting and enforcement activities.* A similar provision is found in *HR 3704,* which refers to this as a safe harbor.

medical service organization (MSO):   A central service, often offered by a hospital to its physicians, which provides administrative services such as insurance and other billing, scheduling of consultations, referrals, and hospitalizations, and stenographic assistance. Only one staff, that of the MSO, needs to become expert in the requirements of the various insurance carriers, and a single computer system is used, with terminals in the physicians' offices.

medical underwriting: See *underwriting (2).*

medically accepted indication: Under the *Health Security Act (HSA)*, the use of a drug which has been approved for such use by the Food and Drug Administration (FDA), or which meets certain other criteria as spelled out in HSA, or for which the carrier meets certain tests specified by the Secretary of Health and Human Services (HHS).

medically underserved area: A rural or urban area which has insufficient health care resources to serve the needs of its population. The term is defined in the Public Health Service Act and used to determine which areas have priority for assistance.

medically underserved population: A population group which has insufficient health care resources to serve its needs.

The group may reside in a *medically underserved area*, or may be a population group with certain attributes; for example, migrant workers, Native Americans, or prison inmates may constitute a medically underserved population. The term is defined in the Public Health Service Act and used to determine which areas have priority for assistance.

Medicare: The federal program which provides health care to persons 65 years of age and older and to others entitled to Social Security benefits. Medicare is administered at the federal level, as contrasted with *Medicaid*, which is administered by the states. Medicare was established in 1965 by amendment to the Social Security Act, the pertinent section of the amendment being "Title XVIII--Health Insurance for the Aged." There are two parts to Medicare:

Medicare, Part A: The hospital care portion (Hospital Insurance Program (HI)) of Medicare. Individuals who (1) are age 65 and over and who qualify for the Social Security "Old Age, Survivors, Disability and Health Insurance Program" or who are entitled to railroad retirement benefits; (2) are under age 65 but have been eligible for disability for more than two years; or (3) qualify for the end stage renal disease (ESRD) program are automatically enrolled in Part A of Medicare. Synonym(s): Hospital Insurance Program (HI).

Medicare, Part B: The part of Medicare through which persons entitled to *Medicare, Part A*, the Hospital Insurance Program, may obtain assistance with payment for physicians' services. Individuals participate voluntarily through enrollment and the payment of a monthly fee.

Medicare and Medicaid magnetized health benefit cards: Under *HR 3080*, the term used for the "health security card (HSC)" proposed in the *Health Security Act (HSA)*.

Medicare fraud and abuse rules: See *fraud and abuse*.

Medicare Geographic Classification Review Board (MGCRB): The board, advisory to the *Health Care Financing Administration (HCFA)*, which reviews applications from hospitals for their classification into one of the three tiers of reimbursement levels available to hospitals under Medicare.

Medicare Insured Group (MIG): An organizational concept allowing businesses or labor unions to distribute Medicare funds to retired employees.

By targeting a specific group of retirees, it is hoped that costs can be lowered through the use of *managed care.*

Medicare SELECT: A new type of *Medicare supplement insurance* which has lower premiums in return for a limited choice by the beneficiaries: they will use only health care providers who have been selected by the insurer as "preferred providers." Medicare SELECT will also pay supplemental benefits for emergency care furnished by providers outside the preferred provider network.

HR 3080 defines Medicare select as a specific type of Medicare supplement (Medigap) policy.

Medicare supplement insurance: Insurance which may be purchased by an individual to add to the benefits provided that individual under Medicare itself. Intelligent purchase of such insurance was virtually impossible until 1992, when *uniform benefit packages*, which standardized benefits for Medicare supplement insurance, were mandated by the federal government. A total of 10 standard plans ("A" through "J") were specified (see the chart on the next page). No insurance company can offer such insurance with benefits below the minimum, Plan A. If an insurance company wants to offer more elaborate benefits, each offering must conform with one of the other nine plans, Plans B through J. Synonym(s): Medigap insurance.

Medicare Volume Performance Standards (MVPS): A type of *expenditure target* which was one element of the *physician payment reform* introduced by the *Omnibus Budget Reconciliation Act of 1989 (OBRA 89).*

medigap insurance: See *Medicare supplement insurance.*

Medigap policy: See *Medicare supplement insurance.*

medisave: See *medical savings account* and *MedAccess plan.*

MGCRB: See *Medicare Geographic Classification Review Board.*

Michel bill (HR 3080): See *Affordable Health Care Now Act of 1993.*

MICRA: See *Medical Injury Compensation Reform Act.*

micro measures: In health care, refers to steps taken to improve the health care provided to individual patients, rather than the health care system. See *macro measures.*

microeconomics: The economic theory which pertains to forces which determine the decisions and actions of individuals, rather than of entire populations. The latter theory is called macroeconomics.

microregulation: Regulation of the health care of patients at the level of the individual institution, physician, and patient. Not only does microregulation interfere with the freedom of all three, but it also significantly increases administrative costs and paperwork, because of the oversight system required to monitor the "behavior" of the physician, patient, and institution.

MIG: See *Medicare Insured Group.*

10 Standard Medicare Supplement Benefit Plans

Core Benefits:	A	B	C	D	E	F	G	H	I	J
Part A Hospital (Days 61-90)	*	*	*	*	*	*	*	*	*	*
Lifetime Reserve Days (91-150)	*	*	*	*	*	*	*	*	*	*
365 Life Hosp. Days — 100%	*	*	*	*	*	*	*	*	*	*
Parts A & B Blood	*	*	*	*	*	*	*	*	*	*
Part B Coinsurance — 20%	*	*	*	*	*	*	*	*	*	*
Additional Benefits:										
Skilled Nursing Facility Coinsurance (Days 21-100)			*	*	*	*	*	*	*	*
Part A Deductible		*	*	*	*	*	*	*	*	*
Part B Deductible			*			*				*
Part B Excess Charges						100%	80%		100%	100%
Foreign Travel Emergency			*	*	*	*	*	*	*	*
At-Home Recovery				*			*		*	*
Prescription Drugs								1	1	2
Preventive Medical Care					*					*

Core Benefits pay the patient's share of Medicare's approved amount for physician services (20%) after $100 annual deductible, the patient's cost of a long hospital stay ($163/day for days 60-90), $326/day for days 91-150, all approved costs not paid by Medicare after day 150 to a total of 365 days lifetime), and charges for the first 3 pints of blood not covered by Medicare.
Two prescription drug benefits are offered:
1. a "basic" benefit with $250 annual deductible, 50% coinsurance and a $1,250 maximum annual benefit (Plans H and I above), and
2. an "extended" benefit (Plan J above) containing a $250 annual deductible, 50% coinsurance and a $3,000 maximum annual benefit.
From the *1992 Guide to Health Insurance for People with Medicare*, Medicare Publications, Health Care Financing Administration, 6325 Security Boulevard, Baltimore, MD 21207.

Minnesota plan: In 1992 Minnesota enacted "HealthRight" legislation which is being closely watched in the health care reform discussions. The law (1) establishes a commission whose goal is at least a 10% decrease in the annual rate of increase in health care costs; (2) establishes a voluntary, state-subsidized insurance called MinnesotaCare which is available to low-income persons on a sliding scale proportional to income, with a maximum premium, and with state subsidy; (3) places reform regulations on insurance companies to prevent such practices as exclusion of pre-existing conditions and to provide *portability* of benefits and work toward standardization of rates across contracts; and (4) gives special attention to the unique problems of rural communities. The stipulation that physicians practicing within state-approved guidelines are given defense thereby in malpractice litigation is attracting considerable attention. Minnesotans point out that the law outlines a state's responsibility to provide a health care system rather than approaching the problem from the citizen's right to health care.

MIS (1): See *management information system* under *information system*.

MIS (2): Manager of information systems.

Mitchell bill: See *Health Security Act (HSA)*.

monosonistic: From monopsony, a market in which there is only one buyer, and that buyer exerts a disproportionate influence on the market; a special type of oligopsony, in which there are a few buyers with such influence.

Moynihan bill (S 1775): See *Health Security Act (HSA)*.

MPKC: See *Management Problem-Knowledge Coupler* under *Problem-Knowledge Coupler*.

MSO: See *medical service organization*.

multihospital system: A term which technically pertains to two or more hospitals under a single governing body. In current usage, "multihospital system" also applies to a number of formal and informal arrangements among hospitals, varying from sharing of one or two services, through a variety of leasing, sponsoring, and contract-managing schemes, to full-blown single ownership of two or more facilities. Synonym(s): chain organization, hospital chain.

multipayer system: A health care reform approach which uses a number of *payers*, usually both private and public. The *German-style system* is a multipayer system. See also *single-payer plan*.

multiple employer welfare arrangement: Under *HR 3080* and *HR 3704*, a specifically defined plan under the *Employee Retirement Income Security Act (ERISA)* of 1974 which is included in health care reform plans when it provides defined health benefits. Such plans may be insured or uninsured.

MVPS: See *Medicare Volume Performance Standards*.

N

NAIC: See *National Association of Insurance Commissioners*.

National Association of Insurance Commissioners (NAIC): The association of state-elected or state-appointed insurance commissioners in the U.S. Under certain of the health care reform proposals, e.g., *HR 3080*, NAIC is to be given the first opportunity to provide certain services and analyses to the Secretary [of Health and Human Services]. If the services--actuarial analyses, for example--are not delivered within a specified time, the Secretary is given other options for obtaining the necessary information and advice.

National Commission to Prevent Infant Mortality (NCPIM): A Washington DC-based organization promoting "resource mothers," the U.S. name for the individuals who, in the United Kingdom, are called "health visitors." These persons guide mothers through child care and also through the health care system. An effort of NCPIM is the Resource Mothers Development Project (RMDP), which seeks to introduce resource mothers into every community to help needy pregnant women and their children. The duties of resource mothers would appear to be identical to those of public health nurses. NCPIM is sponsored by Nestle.

National Council of Community Hospitals (NCCH): An association of over 150 *nonprofit* community hospitals and health care systems, large and small, whose members provide more than 50,000 hospital beds nationwide and are located in 30 states. NCCH is dedicated to the survival and increasing efficiency of community hospitals, which deliver 80% of the hospital services provided to patients in the U.S. Many of these hospitals also conduct programs of professional education and research. National Council of Community Hospitals, 1700 K Street, Suite 906, Washington, DC 20006-3817. Telephone 202-728-0830.

national fraud and abuse data bank: Under *HR 3704*, a data bank to be established by the Attorney General, into which are deposited the information required in the national health care fraud and abuse data collection program, to be established under the Act.

National Fund for Medical Research: Under *HR 3704*, a new fund in the United States Treasury.

National Health Board (NHB): Under the *Health Security Act (HSA)*, a new body to be created in the executive branch of the federal government. Its duties would be interpretive, administrative, and advisory with regard to (1) the comprehensive benefit package; (2) cost containment; (3) "coverage and families"; (4) quality management and improvement; (5) information standards; (6) participating state requirements; (7) determination of "premium class factors;" (8) development of risk adjustment methodology; (9) "encouraging reasonable pricing of breakthrough drugs"; (10) financial requirements; (11) health plan grievance procedures; (12) review and approval of state systems; and (13) carry out certain duties in the absence of state systems.

national health care: An approach to health care reform in which the government pays for and delivers health care. Sometimes used (inaccurately) as a synonym for the *Canadian-style system.*

National Health Informatics Commission (NHIC): Under *HR 3704*, a panel of 15 members with special expertise to advise and make recommendations to the *Health Care Data Panel (HCDP)* on all aspects of the *national health care data interchange system.*

national health insurance: As presently used, means an insurance program which is based on "citizenship rather than employment" (see Starr, P. *The Logic of Health-Care Reform*, Whittle Direct Books, 1992). National health insurance is not necessarily a governmental program, but rather access to a "mainstream standard of coverage." A method of determining eligibility of residents who are not citizens to obtain the insurance would have to be worked out. Contrast with *nationalized health insurance*.

national health service: An approach to health care reform in which the government owns the hospitals and employs the physicians, thereby becoming the *provider* of health services. Synonym(s): nationalized health care.

National Health Service Corps (NHSC): A federal program to provide financial assistance for persons who are preparing for health professions, and in return obligating them to serve in areas where there is a shortage of health care professionals. They are placed by the U.S. Public Health Service. Also known simply as The Corps. See also *medically underserved area* and *medically underserved population*.

national measures of quality performance (NMQP): Under the *Health Security Act (HSA)*, a set of standards to be developed by the *National Quality Management Council (NQMC)* and used by NQMC to assess the provision of health care services and access to such services. The measures will provide information on "1) access to health care services by consumers, 2) appropriateness of health care services provided to consumers, 3) outcomes of health care services and procedures, 4) health promotion, 5) prevention of diseases, disorders, and other health conditions, and 6) consumer satisfaction with care."

National Privacy and Health Data Advisory Council (NPHDAC): U n d e r the *Health Security Act (HSA)*, a 15-member body set up to advise the *National Health Board (NHB)*.

National Quality Consortium (NQC): Under the *Health Security Act (HSA)*, an 11-member group appointed by the *National Health Board (NHB)* with duties to establish programs for the continuing education of health care professionals, advise on research priorities, oversee the development of regional professional foundations, and consult with the *National Quality Management Council (NQMC)* on *national measures of quality performance (NMQP)*.

National Quality Management Council (NQMC): Under the *Health Security Act (HSA)*, a 15-member body appointed by the President to (1) administer the National Quality Management Program (NQMP), and provide stipulated reports to Congress and the public pertaining to the performance of health plans and health alliances; (2) advise the National Health Board (NHB), and (3) perform certain other duties, including directing the Administrator for Health Care Policy and Research as to development and dissemination of practice guidelines; research on health care quality; conducting consumer surveys including those designed to evaluate the impact of HSA on the general population; and establish and oversee regional professional foundations.

National Quality Management Program (NQMP): A performance-based program designed to enhance the quality, appropriateness, and effectiveness of health care services, and also access to those services. NQMP will be a function of the *National Quality Management Council (NQMC)*, and in performing this function, NQMC will use the *national measures of quality performance* which it is charged to develop.

nationalized health care: See *national health service.*

nationalized health insurance: An approach to health care reform in which the government is the *single-payer;* see *payer* and *single-payer plan.* Contrast with *national health insurance.*

NCCH: See *National Council of Community Hospitals.*

NCPIM: See *National Commission to Prevent Infant Mortality.*

need-adjusted population: Under *HR 3704,* the product of the total population of a state multiplied by its need index.

need index: Under *HR 3704,* an index (mathematical) developed from the poverty index and other factors of the State.

negligence: The failure to exercise reasonable care. In addition to its ordinary meaning, negligence has a specific legal meaning; it is one kind of *tort* which results in legal *liability (1).* The tort of negligence requires a duty to exercise reasonable care; a failure to exercise such care; and an injury which was proximately caused by that failure. One may commit a careless act, but if no one is injured as a result, there is no "negligence" as far as legal liability is concerned.

professional negligence: In the context of health care, professional negligence is the failure of a professional to exercise that degree of care and skill practiced by other professionals of similar skill and training (and, in some states, in the same geographic locality) under similar circumstances (see *standard of care (2)*). Such lack of care alone, however, will not result in legal liability; there must be an injury to the patient, and the injury must have been caused by the negligent act.

negotiated fee schedule: A *fee* schedule determined through collective bargaining. This would be used to set global budgets (see *global budgeting.* The American Medical Association (AMA) wants the Federal Trade Commission (FTC) to permit organized medicine to represent physicians in such negotiations. Synonym(s): negotiated payment schedule.

negotiated payment schedule: See *negotiated fee schedule.*

negotiated underwriting: See *underwriting (1).*

neo-no-fault compensation: See *patients' compensation* under *compensation.*

network: An undefined (or very broadly defined) term popular in health care reform discussions. A good idea of its lack of specificity is the discussion in *Joint Commission Perspectives*, September-October 1993. One single criterion seems to apply, that networks should " . . . have a locus of centralized direction, that is, central staff that coordinates enrollee activities, and either delivers or arranges for health care service to individuals. These networks are expected to take a variety of forms, ranging from health maintenance organizations and other managed care organizations, to vertically and horizontally integrated community-based systems, to federations of organizations that have united to cooperate in the delivery of services. Networks also encompass the accountable health plans contemplated in various health care reform proposals."

local network: A term without specific meaning, being used to cover a wide variety of arrangements, informal as well as formal, among providers of health care in a local area. The intent is to form "integrated health care plans" or systems, another term covering a wide variety of arrangements.

provider network: Defined by the Joint Commission on Accreditation of Healthcare Organizations (JCAHO) as " . . . an organized health care delivery system that provides an integrated range of services, often to an identified group of patients." In May 1993 JCAHO announced its intention to develop standards for evaluating such networks. Drafting was done, and the proposed standards entered the formal review process in November 1993, with the intent to present them to the Board of Commissioners for final approval in January 1994. A manual for accrediting networks is planned for early 1994.

NHB: See *National Health Board.*

NHIC: See *National Health Informatics Commission.*

NHSC: See *National Health Service Corps.*

Nickels bill: See *S 1743.*

NMQP: See *national measures of quality performance.*

no-fault: See *no-fault compensation* under *compensation.*

noetic: Originating or existing in the intellect or the spiritual world. There are an increasing number of health care organizations which are emphasizing the integration of science and spirituality in order to enhance the "healing force," joining scientific medicine with a spiritual or noetic dimension, to create whole person and whole community health care.

nondiscrimination based on health status: Under *HR 3704,* a qualified health plan " . . . may not deny, limit, or condition the coverage under (or benefits of) the plan based on the health status, claims experience, receipt of health care, execution of an advanced directive, medical history, or lack of evidence of insurability, of an individual."

nonprofit: A corporation whose "profits" (excess of income over expense) are used for purposes of the organization rather than returned to shareholders or investors as dividends. "Nonprofit" does not necessarily mean "tax-exempt"; see *tax exempt.* See also *501(c)(3).*

NPHDAC: See *National Privacy and Health Data Advisory Council.*

NQC: See *National Quality Consortium.*

NQMC: See *National Quality Management Council.*

NQMP: See *National Quality Management Program.*

nursing home: An institution which provides continuous nursing and other services to patients who are not acutely ill, but who need nursing and personal services as *inpatients*. A nursing home has permanent facilities and an organized professional staff.

Nursing Home Quality Reform Act (NHQRA): Passed as part of the Omnibus Budget Reconciliation Act of 1987 (OBRA 87), the NHQRA has had a great impact on *long-term care* facilities. It required substantial upgrading in the quality of nursing homes and increased enforcement in several areas including discrimination against Medicaid recipients, licensed nurse coverage, and federal standards for nursing home administrators. A recent article reported substantial reduction in antipsychotic drug use in nursing homes with the implementation of this Act.

O

OBRA 87: See *Omnibus Budget Reconciliation Act of 1987.*

OBRA 89: See *Omnibus Budget Reconciliation Act of 1989.*

off-label use: Under *HR 3222*, the use of a drug if the medical indication for which it is used is listed in one of three compendia: (1) American Hospital Formulary Service Drug Information, (2) American Medical Association Drugs Evaluations, or (3) United States Pharmacopeia Drug Information.

Office of Health Care Competition Policy (OHCCP): Under *HR 3704*, an office to be established by the Secretary [of Health and Human Services] to assist the Secretary in developing policies relating to the competitive and collaborative activities of providers of health care service.

Office of Health Technology Assessment (OHTA): One component of the *Agency for Health Care Policy and Research (AHCPR)* of the Public Health Service (PHS), Department of Health and Human Services (DHHS). OHTA evaluates, on request from the Health Care Financing Administration (HCFA), the risks, benefits, and clinical effectiveness of new or unestablished medical technologies that are being considered for coverage under Medicare. The assessments of OHTA form the basis for recommendations to HCFA as to coverage policy decisions under Medicare. "Health Technology Assessment Reports" are produced from the data collected and analyzed by OHTA. The reports are available without charge from the National Technical Information Service (NTIS).

Office of Management and Budget (OMB): The agency in the federal executive branch which prepares and monitors the budget.

Office of Private Health Care Coverage (OPHCC): Under *HR 3080,* a body with a Director and an Advisory Committee of 17 members which shall provide an annual report to the Secretary of Health and Human Services on evaluation of health care coverage reform.

OHCCP: See *Office of Health Care Competition Policy.*

OHTA: See *Office of Health Technology Assessment.*

oligopsony: A market in which there are only a few buyers who exert great influence on the market. A special case of oligopsony is a monopsony, in which there is only one buyer.

OMB: See *Office of Management and Budget.*

Omnibus Budget Reconciliation Act of 1987 (OBRA 87): A federal act which, among other things, included the *Nursing Home Quality Reform Act.*

Omnibus Budget Reconciliation Act of 1989 (OBRA 89): A federal act which, among other things, called for significant *physician payment reform* and increased funding for health care effectiveness research.

OMSB: See *Outcomes Management System Information Board.*

On Lok: Short for On Lok Senior Health Services, a program in San Francisco's Chinatown which enables severely disabled and frail older persons to remain at home rather than be placed in nursing homes. (On Lok means "happy home.")

OP: See *outpatient.*

open enrollment: An limited time period, usually occurring annually, during which individuals are given the opportunity to enroll in a health care insurance plan without medical screening, and without regard to their health status. Open enrollment is a characteristic of some *Blue Cross and Blue Shield* plans and some *health maintenance organizations* (HMOs). The time period is limited in order to minimize the potential for *adverse selection.* Open enrollment is an effort to approach *community rating* (see *rating*).

OPHCC: See *Office of Private Health Care Coverage.*

Oregon plan: In 1989 Oregon passed the Oregon Health Plan designed to insure that all citizens would receive at least basic health care. One part would expand Medicaid coverage to all residents below the federal poverty level. This would be done by prioritizing services to be offered on the basis of the benefit of each of some nearly 750 "diagnosis-treatment (or condition-treatment) pairs" which were carefully developed by physicians, other providers, and with significant community input. The Oregon Health Services Commission included *all* conditions which are encountered in caring for the Oregon population. The diagnosis-treatment pairs were ranked from highest priority (pairs expected to have full recovery from established treatments, such as acute appendicitis with appendectomy) to lowest priority (pairs such as minor cosmetic surgery). Actuarial analysis then determined how far down the list of pairs the available funds would go in providing the services to *all the population*. Those pairs above the line would be funded, those below would not.

A second part of the plan would require employers to cover employees and their dependents. A third would require the small insurance market to form an all-payers' *high risk pool* (see *risk pool*).

At the time of enactment of the law, Medicaid in Oregon was only able to cover 58% of the population below the federal poverty level; the goal is to cover 100% of this population, even though coverage will be more "basic." In 1991 the Oregon Department of Human Resources submitted to the Health Care Financing Administration (HCFA) a proposal to implement the resulting plan as a 5-year demonstration project to begin in January 1992. The Clinton administration approved trial of the plan (with minor modifications) in March 1993. The plan went into operation on February 1, 1994, for the Medicaid population, using the "Prioritized List of Physical Health Services" dated April 19, 1993, and covering services down through line 565 of that list. Oregon plans in 1995 to use the more comprehensive list of services, the "Prioritized List of Integrated Health Services," which also contains mental health and chemical dependency services. These 49 diagnosis-treatment pairs, inserted according to their priorities in the overall list, brought to total to 745. In the "Integrated List" the cutoff would be at line 606, which is the same "pair" as line 565 in the Physical Services List. See the chart on pages 102-103.

organizational liability: See *liability (1)*.

out-of-area: See *out-of-network*.

out-of-network: An adjective applied to a provider or a service when the provider is not a part of the health care network (or system) or the service is not available within the network, and thus the cost has not been the subject of prior agreement. May also be called "out-of-area." The antonym is, of course, "in-network."

outcome: A term used very loosely, particularly in evaluating patient care and the health care system and its components. When used for populations or the health care system, it typically refers to changes in birth or death rates, or some similar global measure. In contrast, it may refer to the "outcome" (finding) of a given diagnostic procedure. It may also refer to cure of the patient, restoration of function, or extension of life, sometimes with an attempt to introduce into the calculation some quantification of the *quality of life*.

When used in *quality management*, it is difficult to find in what dimensions and at what time in the history of the patient's problem outcome is to be determined. It is commonly stated that three things can be measured in relation to quality: structure, process, and outcome. "Structure" refers to resources, and "process" refers to the things done for the patient. There is a tendency on the part of some individuals to take an "either-or" position, to the effect that one need only be concerned with one of the three dimensions. This tendency is not logical; all three must be considered. Clearly, certain structure is needed; and equally clearly, there is no way to change

	Oregon Health Plan Prioritized List of Physical Health Services[1] – April 19, 1993	
Rank[3]	Diagnosis[2]	Treatment[2]
	"TOP 11"	
1	severe/moderate head injury: hematoma/edema with loss of consciousness	medical & surgical treatment
2	insulin-dependent diabetes mellitus	medical therapy
3	peritonitis	medical & surgical treatment
4	acute glomerulonephritis: with lesion of rapidly progressive glomerulonephritis	medical therapy including dialysis
5	pneumothorax & hemothorax	tube thoracostomy/thoracotomy, medical therapy
6	hernia with obstruction and/or gangrene	repair
7	Addison's disease	medical therapy
8	flail chest	medical & surgical treatment
9	appendicitis	appendectomy
10	ruptured spleen	repair/splenectomy/incision
11	tuberculosis	medical therapy
. . .	CUTOFF AREA FEBRUARY 1994	
561	equinus deformity of foot, acquired	arthrotomy
562	internal derangement of knee	arthroscopic repair, medical therapy
563	Reiter's Disease	medical therapy
564	stenosis of nasolacrimal duct (acquired)	dacryocystorhinostomy
565	peripheral nerve disorders (non-injury) [Last covered condition-treatment]	neuroplasty
566	absence of breast after mastectomy as treatment for neoplasm	breast reconstruct
567	cavus deformity of foot; flat foot; polydactyly & syndactyly of toes	medical therapy, orthotic
568	peripheral enthesopathies	surgical treatment
569	peripheral enthesopathies	medical therapy
570	diaphysitis	medical therapy

Oregon Health Plan Prioritized List of Physical Health Services (continued)		
...	"BOTTOM 11"	
686	benign neoplasm of external female genital organs	excision
687	benign neoplasm of male genital organs	medical therapy
688	xerosis	medical therapy
689	sarcoidosis	medical therapy
690	congenital cystic lung — severe	lung resection
691	ichthyosis	medical therapy
692	lymphedema	medical therapy, other operation on lymph channel
693	other aplastic anemias	medical therapy
694	tubal dysfunction & other causes of infertility	in-vitro fertilization, gift
695	hepatorenal syndrome	medical therapy
696	spastic dysphonia	medical therapy

[1] The complete list of diagnosis-treatment pairs and other information about the plan may be obtained from the Oregon Department of Human Resources, Office of Medical Assistance Programs, Human Resources Bldg. — 3rd Floor, 500 Summer St. NE, Salem, OR 97310-1014, telephone 503-378-2263 (there is a charge).

[2] Note that a given condition might have more than one possible treatment, and that a given treatment might be used for more than one condition. Thus conditions and treatments could appear more than once in the list (see also footnote 3). "Medical therapy" is the treatment component of many of the diagnosis-treatment pairs.

[3] Among the factors taken into consideration by the Oregon Health Services Commission in ranking the diagnosis-treatment pairs were the following: (1) When there were two different treatments for the same condition, Oregon physicians may have judged one more effective than another: the more effective treatment was, of course, ranked higher. For example, a laryngeal polyp with "surgical treatment" is number 447, with "medical therapy," it is 723; (2) a condition which will simply "run its course" without therapy is given low ranking; (3) purely cosmetic treatments are given low ranking; (4) when a disease is "staged," a low "stage," if that means greater likelihood for cure, will call for a higher position in the list; and (5) when a condition is complicated by occurring in an immunocompromised patient, it is given a higher rank than otherwise.

outcome except through changing process, since "outcome 'tells on' process." See also *health outcome*.

Outcomes Management System Information Board (OMSB): One of three advisory boards to the *National Health Board (NHB)* proposed by the *Jackson Hole Group*. The OMSB, if the proposal is implemented, will "establish national data system for patient outcomes and other quality measures. Sets data collection and reporting standards for AHPs [*accountable health plans*]. Will oversee data centers and data evaluation. Will consist of provider, insurer, consumer and employer representatives."

outcomes research: Research attempting to evaluate the relative benefits of various kinds of treatment and medical care by measuring the outcomes of the care. The basic question asked is "Does Treatment A or Treatment B give the better outcome?" This is, of course, followed by "How much better is the one than the other?" and "How costly is the treatment with the better outcome?" And finally, there follows an evaluation of the cost/benefit relationship.

outlier: A patient who requires an unusually long stay or whose stay generates unusually great cost. The term is used in the *prospective payment system (PPS)*. About five or six percent of the budgets for regional and national rates have been set aside for payments for outliers. Outliers provide an escape hatch for the hospital, because they allow the hospital to negotiate for a fee higher than the *diagnosis related group (DRG)* price which would otherwise apply to the patient. Outliers are of two kinds:

cost outlier: An unusually costly case.

stay outlier: An unusually long stay. Also called day outlier.

out-of-pocket cap: See *cap*.

outpatient (OP): A person who receives care without taking up lodging in a care institution.

P

PAC (1): See *preadmission certification*.

PAC (2): See *products of ambulatory care*.

PACE: See *Program of All-Inclusive Care for the Elderly*.

palliative care: Treatment to relieve or reduce pain, discomfort, or other symptoms of disease, but not to cure. See also *comfort care*.

panel: A group of individuals, such as physicians. The term is used for groups such as the physicians who form a *preferred provider organization (PPO)*, and those who are convened to review a grant application.

paradigm: One's view of "the way things are"; an implicit framework within which "everything" fits or is understood. In science, for example, one's "world view" restricts what problems are considered legitimate for study and what methods are acceptable to pursue them. Sir Isaac Newton's "laws" of gravity and motion, developed in the 17th and 18th century, governed much of the scientific thought for nearly two centuries. Einstein's paradigm not only explained the same phenomena, but also opened the way for new thought. When people thought the earth was flat, this paradigm governed thinking about stars, oceans, and travel. Proof that the earth was a sphere released entirely new thinking. See *paradigm shift*.

paradigm shift: The change in one's "world view" in moving from one *paradigm* to another: replacing an old paradigm with a new one. Such a change may take a lot of energy, and usually has far-reaching consequences.

Among the paradigm shifts emerging today in health are: (1) from the view that knowledge processing is limited to the human mind, plus "paper and pencil," to the view that knowledge processing can be successfully extended through use of computer technology; (2) from the view that the physician should assume a "paternal" role of caring and making decisions for the patient, to the view that empowered patients are competent to collaborate in their own health care and that, in fact, many wish to and can *direct* their own care; (3) from the view that the government is responsible for the health of the community, to the view that the community itself is responsible; and (4) from the view that health care providers are there to provide "health care," to the view that "health" rather than "health care" is their goal.

parameter (1): A term gaining the favor of physicians in referring to statements which delineate the ways in which it is acceptable for physicians to treat patients. Recent American Medical Association (AMA) statements indicate an interpretation of the term "standard" as referring to a rigid rule, any deviation from which is subject to censure, and "parameter" as referring to "an acceptable range of options." It would seem that any properly drawn standards should allow adaptation to the peculiar problem presented by the individual patient, the skills of the physician, and the resources available. The argument apparently is over the breadth of the standard rather than the concept that certain practice is acceptable, but other practice is not. See *guidelines (2)*.

practice parameter: See *guidelines (2)*.

parameter (2): "The thing measured," as in "*monitor parameter*."

monitor parameter: Anything being kept track of systematically. The term originated in connnection with quality assessment, in which certain key data, such as death rates, infection rates, average length of stay, and the like, were identified as giving such useful information that running records should be kept, that is, that they should be monitored. The infection itself is the "thing," or parameter, the numbers of infections are its "value" and are the statistics monitored.

Partnership for Long Term Care (PLTC): A experimental long-term care program supported by the Robert Wood Johnson Foundation in four states (1993) (CA, CT, IN, NY) in which individuals who buy Partnership "certified policies" may keep assets equal to the amount their insurance paid out and still receive Medicaid benefits. Medicaid is used as reinsurance for the certified policies.

PAS: See *preadmission screening*.

PAT: See *preadmission testing*.

patient: A person who has established a contractual relationship with a health care provider for that provider to care for that person. A patient may or may not be ill or injured. A patient who is ill or injured, or who otherwise presents a health problem, is often referred to as a "case."

patient card: A card which stores in magnetic or optical form information about a patient which can be read by an electronic device. In general, there are two applications of this technology in health care:

(1) Personal identification cards similar to credit cards. The typical storage medium is a magnetic strip. This type of card is apparently the type envisioned in the *Health Security Act (HSA)* which calls it the "health security card (HSC)" and stipulates that it would carry, in addition to the bearer's identification, information as to insurance benefits. *HR 3080* calls the card the "Medicare and Medicaid magnetized health benefit card."

(2) The second application is for carrying the individual's medical record. Credit card sized patient cards are on the market, for example, which, using optical storage technology, can carry 40-80 megabytes of data, i.e., the entire content of a large medical record, including not only text but also images and sound.

patient care manager (PCM): The person who is responsible for determining the services to be provided to a patient and coordinating the provision of the appropriate care. The purposes of the PCM's function are: (1) to improve the quality of care by considering the whole patient, that is, all the patient's problems and other relevant factors; (2) to ensure that all necessary care is obtained; and (3) to reduce unnecessary care (and cost). When, as is often the case, the PCM is a physician, she or he is a primary care physician and usually must, except in an emergency, give the first level of care to the patient before the patient is permitted to be seen by a secondary care physician (specialist). In fact, the PCM must refer the patient for the secondary care. Synonym(s): care manager, gatekeeper, gateway.

It has been suggested that the term "PCM" replace the widely-used term "gatekeeper," but "gatekeeper" is likely to be retained as well.

The *Eutaw Group*, in its *community care plan (CCP)*, has suggested the term "gateway" to replace "gatekeeper." The contention is that the patient should be welcomed into the health care system and helped; "gatekeeper" suggests to them a role of keeping people out. Access to the CCP is via a generalist, who may or may not be a physician, although physician oversight is planned.

patient-directed care: A trend in medical practice stemming from the concept that patients should be empowered to make choices (decisions) as to their own health and health care. In patient-directed care, the physician advises and collaborates with the patient in determining the steps to be taken to discover the causes of problems and in treating those problems. See also *patient empowerment*.

patient dumping: See *dumping*.

Patient Self-Determination Act (PSDA): An act passed, by the U.S. Congress in 1990, which became effective in December 1991, which requires most hospitals, nursing homes, and other patient care institutions to ask all admitted patients whether they have made *advance directives* as to their wishes as to the use of medical interventions for themselves in case of the loss of their own decision-making capacity. The institution is required to furnish each patient with written information about advance directives.

patients' compensation: See *compensation*.

pay or play: See *employer mandate* under *mandate*.

payer: An organization or person who furnishes the money to pay for the provision of health care services. A payer may be the government (for example, Medicare), a nonprofit organization (such as Blue Cross/Blue Shield (BC/BS)), commercial insurance, or some other entity. In common usage, "payer" most often means *third party payer* (see below).

third party payer: A *payer* who neither receives nor gives the care (the patient and the provider are the first two parties). The third party payer is usually an insurance company, a *prepayment plan*, or a *government agency*. Organizations which are self-insured are also considered third parties. Third party payers are increasingly employers, who try to save the money paid to insurance companies or other third parties.

payment: The act of paying or the amount paid for health care services. See also *copayment*.

PCM: See *patient care manager*.

Peer Review Organization (PRO): An organization set up as a part of the *prospective payment system (PPS)* to carry out certain review functions under contract from the *Health Care Financing Administration (HCFA)*. PROs are external to the hospital; some were formerly *Professional Standards Review Organizations (PSROs)* and the functions of PROs are similar to those performed by PSROs.

The duties of the PRO include, for example: determining whether the medical records of Medicare patients support the diagnoses and procedures stated in the claims submitted; determining whether a changing pattern of care in a hospital, as reflected in its claims submitted, represents an actual change in the kinds of patients or their treatment, or is a fictitious result of the claims submission and reporting system; reviewing the medical necessity of DRG *outliers*; reviewing cardiac pacemaker implantations; and attempting to achieve certain changes in performance in hospitals within the jurisdiction of the PRO. A PRO is not the same as a hospital or medical society peer review committee.

Pepper Commission: An advisory body which in 1990 made recommendations as to universal health insurance coverage for both acute care and long term care, and recommended the *play or pay* method of financing (see *mandate*). Most of the members of the Commission were congressional leaders. The official name of the Commission was the U.S. Bipartisan Commission on Comprehensive Health Reform.

periodic interim payment (PIP): A system of providing Medicare funds to *providers* on a regular basis. Periodic payments may be made monthly or semi-monthly to a hospital, home health agency, or skilled nursing facility in the Medicare program, based on the institution's estimated annual Medicare revenue. Adjustments are made later when actual revenue figures become available. Such a system of payment is also sometimes employed by other *payers*.

personal assistance expenses: Under the *Health Security Act (HSA)*, such expenses are (1) those for assistance with activities of daily living within or outside the home; (2) homemaker/chore services incidental to (1) above; (3) assistance with life skills for a person with cognitive impairment; (4) communication services; (5) work-related support services; (6) coordination of personal assistance services; (7) assistive technology and devices, including assessment for their need and training family members; and (8) modification of the principal place of abode.

PERT: See *program evaluation and review technique.*

PHO: See *physician-hospital organization.*

physician-hospital organization (PHO): A generic term for a "new breed" of organizations (not joint ventures) which are being developed between physicians and hospitals so that a single organization, a PHO, can contract with a purchaser, such as an industry, an insurance company, or a *health alliance (HA)*, to provide physician, hospital, and other health care services under a single contract, or for a single negotiated *capitation* fee. Such organizations are, in effect, providing insurance benefits and assuming the risks involved. Critical actuarial analysis is required for success; reinsurance for expensive services is usually required. See, for example, *Hospital Health Plan (HHP)*.

physician payment reform (PPR): A basic change in the way physicians are paid for services for Medicare patients, mandated by the *Omnibus Budget Reconciliation Act of 1989 (OBRA 89)*, effective 1 January 1992. Prior to that date, payment was based on the actual, *customary, prevailing, reasonable charge (or fee) (CPR)*. Replacing that method, the new method is based on a *resource-based relative value scale (RBRVS)*. One intent of the change is to reduce the premium (high fees) put on *procedures*, typically done by specialists, and increase the reimbursement for *cognitive services* (see *service*), such as evaluation and diagnosis and patient management, services provided mainly by primary care physicians.

A second component of the reform is application of *Medicare Volume*

Performance Standards (MVPS), targets against which physician's spending will be measured. If a physician's standard is exceeded, the next year his or her rate of fee increase will be reduced.

A third component of the reform is a *cap* on the out-of-pocket charges which may be made to beneficiaries.

physician shortage area: A *medically underserved area* which is particularly short of physicians. The term is defined in the Public Health Service Act and used to determine which areas have priority for assistance.

Physicians' Current Procedural Terminology (CPT, CPT-94, etc.): A publication of the *American Medical Association (AMA)*, containing its *classification (1)* of *procedures* and *services*, primarily those carried out by physicians. It is widely used for *coding* in billing and payment for physicians' services. Each "package" of physician services (for example, care for a fracture--including diagnosis, setting the fracture, and putting on and removing the splint) is given one code number and commands one fee for the package. In contrast to *CPT, ICD-9-CM*, the classification used for hospital coding of diagnoses and procedures, has separate codes for each of the four factors: diagnosis, setting the fracture, applying the cast, and removing the cast.

CPT is similar in theory to the *diagnosis related groups* (DRGs) (which currently apply to hospital--not physician--care) in that both are built on the "one code, one fee" basis.

Although the fourth edition of *CPT* appeared in 1977 (at which time it was called "CPT-4"), it has been revised repeatedly since then, and now the volume is labelled annually, for example "*CPT-1994*."

Physician's Payment Review Commission (PhysPRC): A federal advisory body set up to provide input to the *Health Care Financing Administration (HCFA)* regarding methods of saving money in the payment of physicians for *services* to Medicare patients.

PhysPRC: See *Physician's Payment Review Commission.*

PIP: See *periodic interim payment.*

PKCoupler: See *Problem-Knowledge Coupler.*

planning: The analysis of needs, demands, and resources, followed by the proposal of steps to meet the demands and needs by use of the current resources and obtaining other resources as necessary.

community-based planning: Planning in which the attempt is made to have the planning initiative in the local community rather than external to the community itself.

comprehensive health planning (CHP): Attempts to coordinate environmental measures, health education, health care, and occupational and other health efforts to achieve the greatest results in a community.

health planning: Planning for a health care facility, a health program, a defined geographic area, or a population. Health planning may be carried out by the organization itself or by a planning agency. When it is carried out for an area, and the people in the area itself furnish the initiative, it is called "community-based planning."

joint planning: Planning carried out jointly by two or more institutions, which may or may not envision sharing of services and facilities.

strategic planning: A term derived from "strategy" in the military sense; *planning* which is long-range, and which is intended to lay out the nature and sequence of the steps to be taken to achieve the large goals of the organization. In traditional thinking, strategic planning should precede the development of the *tactics* with which it is implemented. A current insight is that a successful strategy can only be developed after the available tactics are assessed and used to their maximum.

play or else: See *employer mandate* under *mandate.*

play or pay: See *employer mandate* under *mandate.*

PLTC: See *Partnership for Long Term Care.*

pluralistic system: A system which provides alternatives. The U.S. is described as favoring pluralism, as illustrated by the fact that medical care, for example, can be obtained from solo practitioners or group practices or prepaid health plans.

point of service option (POS): A *health care plan* which allows the employee (*beneficiary*) to select a health provider each time he or she needs medical care, rather than once a year.

POMR: See *problem-oriented medical record.*

Ponte Vedra Group: An informal ad hoc "think tank" founded by John Horty, LLB, President of the *National Council of Community Hospitals (NCCH),* in 1992. Its first position on health care reform is that a single national solution to all the problems is not possible, that the movement already underway in which health care reform is emerging in local communities from the bottom up in response to those communities' specific needs and resources should be facilitated. Certain legislative changes which would encourage local innovation in health care organization and payment are encouraged, as are changes in favor of universal coverage and community rating for health insurance, tort reform, provision of portable benefits, and adoption of antitrust policies which would favor cooperation and collaboration among providers in order to preserve the patient care value system in the health care field.

In addition to these "macro" measures in health care reform, its second position is that every effort should be made to use the emerging technologies which make possible addressing specifically the problems of each individual patient, a "micro" approach to health care reform which promises improved quality for each person, and lowered cost for each encounter.

The Ponte Vedra Group can be reached at the Indigo Institute, 1700 K Street, Suite 906, Washington, DC 20006-3817. Telephone 202-466-4341.

portability: A term sometimes applied to employee benefits, which means that an employee will retain the same benefits under different employers.

Portable benefit plans have often been worked out for nurses, for example, so that when they are employed by different hospitals, they will still accumulate retirement benefits and will have no gaps in their health care coverage.

portable benefits: See *benefits.*

POS: See *point of service option.*

poverty line: Under *HR 3704*, "... the income official poverty line (as defined by the Office of Management and Budget ...) ... applicable to a family of the size involved."

PPA: See *preferred provider arrangement.*

PPO (1): See *preferred provider option.*

PPO (2): See *preferred provider organization.*

PPR: See *physician payment reform.*

PPS (1): See *prospective payment system.*

PPS (2): See *prospective pricing system.*

practice guidelines: See *guidelines (2).*

practice parameters: See *guidelines (2).*

preadmission certification (PAC): A process by which *elective* care which is proposed for a patient is reviewed and approved before the patient is admitted to the hospital. When a PAC program is in effect, the care will not be paid for unless the certification is obtained.

preadmission process for admission: A formal *admission* process (namely, initiating the paperwork) carried out by a hospital prior to doing *preadmission testing (PAT)* for an *elective* admission patient.

preadmission screening (PAS): A program of evaluation of applicants for admission to nursing homes under Medicare. PAS is required in many states. Some states also require preadmission screening for private pay applicants.

preadmission testing (PAT): The carrying out of laboratory and other diagnostic work on an outpatient basis within a few days of hospital *admission* for the patient scheduled for *elective* hospitalization. It is less costly to have the tests performed in this manner and, in some instances, the test results will be such that hospitalization will be avoided or postponed. The hospital usually goes through a formal acceptance of the patient, called the "preadmission process for admission," prior to carrying out the tests.

predatory pricing: A practice by insurers of giving a low rate on health insurance to a low-risk small group or individual, then raising the rates when the insured start filing claims. See also *cherry picking.* Synonym(s): churning the books, price churning.

preexisting condition: A physical or mental condition which has been discovered before an individual applies for health insurance. Insurers often deny insurance to individuals with certain preexisting conditions, or invoke a waiting period, or reject a group unless such individuals are excluded. Health care reform efforts today (1993) insist that there be no exclusion of individuals for such conditions.

preferred provider arrangement (PPA): A form of organization for physician *services*, in a *health care plan*, in which the plan (*third party payer*; see *payer*) establishes a roster of physicians who are believed to be *cost-effective*. All services covered by the plan, when furnished by these physicians, are without charge to the *beneficiary*. The beneficiary may elect care from physicians not on the roster, but if she or he does, at least part of those providers' fees must be paid by the beneficiary (or, in some forms of health insurance programs, by the physicians making up the roster of preferred providers).

preferred provider option (PPO): A form of *health care plan* in which certain physicians are designated by a *third party payer* (see *payer*) as preferred *providers* whom the payer has concluded are the most *cost-effective*. When a *beneficiary* elects to receive care from these physicians, the physicians' charges are paid in full--there is no additional charge to the beneficiary. The beneficiary may elect to obtain care from other physicians, but if he or she does, there is a financial penalty--the beneficiary must pay part of the charges.

preferred provider organization (PPO): An *alternative delivery system (2) (ADS)* designed to compete with *health maintenance organizations* (HMOs) and other delivery systems. A PPO is stated to be an arrangement involving a contract between health care *providers* (both professional and institutional), and organizations such as employers and *third party administrators* (TPAs), under which the PPO agrees to provide health care services to a defined population for predetermined fixed fees. PPOs are distinguished from HMOs and other similar organizations in that: (1) PPO physicians are paid on a *fee-for-service* basis, while in other delivery systems payment is usually by *capitation* or salary; and (2) PPO physicians are not at risk (see *risk (2)*)--the purchaser of the service retains the risk--while HMOs are at risk.

The term "contract provider organization (CPO)" is preferred by the American Medical Association (AMA) for the arrangements discussed here. The term "CPO" might be preferable as a method of distinguishing a preferred provider organization from the other "PPO"--the *preferred provider option*. See also *exclusive provider organization (EPO)*.

prefunding: Under *HR 3080*, paying in advance the contributions which are or will be required to provide health-benefits coverage for annuitants.

prehospital-based professional: See *hospital-based professional*.

premium: A payment required for an insurance policy for a given period of time. Now the term is being used by some in the health care reform movement to refer to a payment required of employers to pay for health care insurance or services.

prenatal care: Care for a pregnant woman in an effort to keep the woman healthy and to maximize the likelihood that the pregnancy will result in a full-term, full birthweight, healthy infant.

prepaid health plan: A *health care plan* in which the insurer agrees, for a fixed fee paid periodically in advance, to provide a specified array of services to the *beneficiary*.

prepayment: Payment in advance. Under a prepayment system, a fee is paid to a *third party payer* (see *payer*), such as a *health maintenance organization (HMO)*, *Blue Cross/Blue Shield (BC/BS)*, or commercial insurance, and the third party agrees to pay for stipulated care when it is provided. The Medicare *voucher system* is a prepayment system.

prepayment plan: A contractual arrangement for health care in which a prenegotiated payment is made in advance, covering a certain time period, and the *provider* agrees, for this payment, to furnish certain services to the *beneficiary*.

President's Task Force on National Health Care: See *Task Force on National Health Reform*.

prevailing: When used in conjunction with physicians' *fees*, "prevailing" refers to the charges made for the *service* in question in the area, provided by physicians of similar specialty qualifications.

prevailing fee: See *customary, prevailing, reasonable charge (or fee) (CPR)*.

preventive health services: Services designed to (1) prevent disease or injury from occurring, (2) detect it early, (3) minimize its progression, or (4) control resulting disability.

price: The amount of money to be paid for something. Each *diagnosis related group (DRG)*, for example, carries a price, the amount of money to be paid for the hospital care of a patient classified to that DRG.

price blending: A method of adjusting a hospital's price for a given *diagnosis related group (DRG)* under the *prospective payment system (PPS)* after comparing the hospital's cost per case for that DRG with the national average for the same DRG. Synonym(s): DRG-specific price blending.

price churning: See *predatory pricing*.

price-elasticity: A condition in which a seller can increase revenue by *reducing* prices (achieved, of course, by increased volume of sales). Under *managed competition*, price-elasticity is a specific goal.

price-inelasticity: A condition in which a seller can increase revenue by *raising* prices. *Managed competition* seeks to avoid price-inelasticity.

primary care: The care by a *primary care physician*. Care requiring more specialized knowledge or skill is obtained by referral from the primary care physician to the specialist (secondary care physician) for consultation or continued care.

   The term is also used to mean the care given at the initial contact of the patient with the health care system or with a health care provider. It usually takes place in an office or other outpatient setting.

Under *HR 3704*, primary care includes " . . . family practice, general internal medicine, and general pediatrics, and may also include obstetrics and gynecology if such care is person-centered, comprehensive care that is not organ or problem specific."

primary care case management: Under *HR 3080*, a program under which " . . . individuals eligible for medical assistance . . . are enrolled with primary case management entities, and are entitled to receive specified health care items and services . . . only as arranged for and approved by such entities."

primary care case management entity: Under *HR 3704*, " . . . a health care provider which A) must be a physician, group of physicians, a Federally qualified health center . . . under a contract with a State to provide services under a primary care case management program; B) receives payment on a fee-for-service basis . . . or . . . on a reasonable cost-per-encounter basis . . . ; C) receives an additional fixed fee per enrollee for a period specified for providing case management services . . . ; and D) is not an entity that is at risk . . . for such case management services."

Under *HR 3080*, such an entity is defined as *not* at risk for the cost of items and services provided.

primary care case management program: Under *HR 3704*, " . . . a program operated by a State agency under which such State agency enters into contracts with primary care case management entities for provision of health care items and services . . . to individuals who are A) eligible for medical assistance under the State plan; B) enrolled with such primary care case management entitles; and C) entitled to receive such specified health . . . [from] such entities."

primary care physician: A physician who specializes in family practice, general internal medicine, general pediatrics, or obstetrics and gynecology. Provides the initial care for a patient, and refers the patient, when appropriate, for secondary (specialist) care.

Private Health Care Coverage: See *Office of Private Health Care Coverage.*

PRO: See *Peer Review Organization.*

problem: A *disease, injury*, or any other condition or situation which brings an individual into contact with the health care system. Certain conditions, such as alcoholism, are not admitted by all to be diseases, but they do bring individuals to health care, as do ill-defined symptoms, behavioral problems, the need for well-person examinations, and the like. This is the usage of the term "problem" in the *problem-oriented medical record (POMR)*.

Chapter XXI of the *International Statistical Classification of Diseases and Related Health Problems (ICD-10)*, entitled "Factors Influencing Health Status and Contact with Health Services," lists among others the following "factors": loss of love relationship (code number Z61), removal from home (Z61), failed exams in school (Z55), stressful work schedule (Z56), and extreme poverty (Z59.5).

problem-oriented medical record (POMR): A medical record organized around the *problems* presented by the patient. The POMR is organized so that the reader can find out *why* the steps in investigation and management were done, as well as the progress made in solving each of the patient's problems. In the traditionally organized medical record, the reader can only find out *what* was done.

Problem-Knowledge Coupler (PKCoupler): Interactive computer software which matches (couples) the significant attributes of a patient's *problem* with the existing literature which has a bearing on the understanding of or solution to that problem. It was invented by Lawrence Weed, MD (he created the *problem-oriented medical record (POMR)*), who saw the need for and how to use the computer to provide a guidance system for the physician.

Information on the patient's problem is fed into the computer, and the physician is instantly presented on the screen the causes in the literature which could explain the patient's symptoms, or the management options, and then can choose the further action to be taken. The patient is ordinarily given the same information and the decisions are made together. Printed copies are provided for the physician and patient (as advisable). Three kinds of PKCouplers have been developed: diagnostic couplers, management couplers, and "baseline" couplers (history, physical examination, and "wellness").

PKCouplers have certain attributes which are especially important in the issues of quality of care and health care reform:

(1) The individual patient's relevant findings regarding the presenting problem provide a patient profile.

(2) The information in the literature on that problem provides the knowledge base against which the patient's profile is compared.

(3) PKCouplers can be kept up to date with the literature (see *guidelines (2)* for discussion of the problems for the physician regarding "practice parameters" or "clinical guidelines": learning of their existence, their revision, and their withdrawal).

(4) PKCouplers in each instance follow a minimalist strategy. They start with thorough, but precisely targeted, history, physical examination, laboratory work, and X-ray. Only if these procedures fail to help the physician narrow the options are more extensive and expensive steps suggested. And if the investigation fails to permit an exact diagnosis, the physician and the patient are both made aware of the limitations of the knowledge available in the literature.

Diagnostic Problem-Knowledge Coupler (DPKC): A Problem-Knowledge Coupler (PKC) which provides a method of constructing a patient database for a given *problem* and then coupling (comparing, by computer) the patient's database (PDB) for that problem with a knowledge database (KDB) for the same problem. The DPKC for a given problem is structured to elicit data items known to be relevant to that problem from the patient's history, examination, investigative findings, response to therapy, and other factors. The KDB for that problem contains information on these same data items maintained current from the medical literature. Once the

PDB is in the computer, which is done as a part of acquiring the data, "coupling," on command, instantly matches the PDB with the KDB and the computer indicates how closely the various diagnoses in the knowledge database for the patient's problem match the findings of the patient.

A special class of Diagnostic PKC is used at the patient's first visit to develop the initial database, which is the patient's profile and opens the patient's personal *problem-oriented medical record (POMR)*. These couplers are "wellness couplers," and couplers for systems review physical examination. If any of the inventories (PDBs) uncovers *problems*, problem-specific DPKCs for these problems guide further investigation and management.

Management Problem-Knowledge Coupler (MPKC): A Problem-Knowledge Coupler (PKC) which provides alternative management paths for the *problem* or diagnosis in question, giving the pros and cons of the alternatives, such as contraindications, relative probability of success, side-effects, and cost. With MPKC, coupling by computer is also instantaneous.

proceduralist: A physician in whose specialty the performance of *procedures*, diagnostic or therapeutic, such as endoscopies and surgical operations, are a significant element. See *service*. Physicians who are not proceduralists have no specific label, but their services are often described as "cognitive" (see *cognitive services* under *service*). Despite advent of the *resource-based relative value scale (RBRVS)* system in *physician payment reform (PPR)*, the medical community still feels that the services provided by proceduralists are rewarded more highly than are cognitive services.

procedure: In medicine, something which is "done" or "carried out" for a patient by a physician or other person. A procedure is usually discrete, and a relatively short time is required for its execution. Procedures are generally either diagnostic or therapeutic (treatment). A diagnostic procedure would be the taking of an X-ray or blood pressure, while a therapeutic procedure might be anything from removing a splinter from a finger to an extensive operation such as repair of a hernia.

A given operation, which might be called a "procedure," is often actually several procedures, and the array of procedures which make up a given operation will vary from patient to patient. For example, cholecystectomy (gall bladder removal) for one patient may include "exploration of the common bile duct," while for another patient, this procedure may be omitted. For this reason, a proper description of an operation requires that its procedures be listed.

In the context of health care financing, there often appears to be a distinction between a "procedure" and a "*service*." However, the terms "procedure" and "service" are often combined without distinction, as in the classification used for payment of physicians' services, *Physicians' Current Procedural Terminology (CPT)*. In the case of a hernia operation, for example, the preoperative care and postoperative care are listed as "services," while the operation itself is called a "procedure"; however, the surgeon includes the preoperative and postoperative care and the operation in one billing for a "procedure." For purposes of health care financing, a "procedure" (or "service") might more accurately be defined as the unit for which a charge is made. Thus, under the "financial" definition, the hernia repair "procedure" would include both preoperative and postoperative care. See also *operating room procedure*, below.

operating room procedure: A term which, on its face, describes a surgical treatment of a patient, performed in the hospital's operating room. However, the term has a special function under the *prospective payment system (PPS)*: if a patient has an "operating room procedure," that patient is placed in a different payment category than a patient in the same *major diagnostic category (MDC)* who does not have an operating room procedure. For the purpose of making this allocation of patients, an arbitrary list of procedures (actually, a list of procedure codes) has been established by the Health Care Financing Administration (HCFA). If the patient's *data set* submitted for payment has a code shown on the HCFA's list as an operating room procedure, that patient is considered to have had an operating room procedure, no matter where the procedure was actually done.

process: The things done (for a patient, for example). It is commonly stated in *quality management* that three things can be measured: structure (resources or organization), process, and outcome. "Structure" refers to resources and organization. "Outcome" is a somewhat vague term that presumably refers to the results of the process. There is a tendency on the part of some individuals to take an "either-or" position, to the effect that one need only be concerned with one of the three dimensions. This tendency is not logical; all three must be considered. Clearly, certain structure is needed; and equally clearly, there is no way to change outcome except through changing process, since, as Juran says, "outcome 'tells on' process."

product liability: See *liability (1)*.

products of ambulatory care (PAC): A *classification (1)* developed by the New York State Ambulatory Care Reimbursement Demonstration Project in 1985 as a "sophisticated ambulatory care product definition." There are 24 PAC categories, into which patient visits are allocated by computer depending on "who the patient is" (type of problem presented) and what is done (resources received).

Professional Standards Review Organization (PSRO): An organization established under federal law to review medical necessity, appropriateness, and quality of services provided to beneficiaries of the Medicare, Medicaid, and *maternal and child health (MCH)* programs. These organizations were physician-sponsored. They have now been replaced in function by *Peer Review Organizations* (PROs) under the current federal program for the administration of Medicare.

program evaluation and review technique (PERT): A process to identify the accomplishments of programs and the time and resources required to move from one accomplishment to the next. The PERT diagram shows the sequence and interrelationship of activities from the beginning to the end of a project. See *critical path*.

Program of All-Inclusive Care for the Elderly (PACE): A program, begun by the federal government in 1986, in which comprehensive *long-term care* programs are being conducted and studied as to their cost effectiveness. Initial reports are that such programs reduce the acute care hospital care required for their participants.

ProPaC: See *Prospective Payment Assessment Commission.*

prospective payment: A term often used as a misnomer for *prospective pricing.* "Prospective pricing" is the term which more accurately denotes the intent of the payment system currently being used for Medicare, which is discussed under *prospective payment system (PPS).*

Under some circumstances, prospective payment for goods or services is made in advance (*prepayment*), either in whole or in partial payments, with adjustments made to the total when the actual amount due is determined. Payment in advance provides cash flow for the payee.

Prospective Payment Assessment Commission (ProPaC): An advisory body established under Medicare to give advice and assistance to the *Health Care Financing Administration (HCFA)* on matters pertaining to the *prospective payment system (PPS)* under which Medicare operates. Advice from ProPaC is not binding on HCFA.

prospective payment system (PPS): The name given the system currently in use for paying for services for Medicare patients (payment for patients "by *diagnosis related group*s (DRGs)"). The idea is that patients are classified into categories (in this case, DRGs) for which prices are negotiated or imposed on the hospital in advance; thus it is actually "prospective pricing" rather than "prospective payment." At present PPS is only applied to hospital care, not physician care, although the idea is the same as a single fixed "package fee" which includes prenatal care, delivery, and postpartum care for a maternity patient, or the inclusion of preoperative care, operation, and postoperative care for an appendectomy patient within one fixed physician's fee. (In fact, the package fee concept is inherent in *Physicians' Current Procedural Terminology (CPT)*, published by the American Medical Association (AMA)). PPS, while not mandated by federal law for payers other than Medicare, is being applied to patients under other health care plans.

PPS is sometimes referred to as the "DRG system." (The letters "PPS" are sometimes translated, incorrectly, to mean a prospective *reimbursement* system.)

prospective pricing: Setting (or agreeing upon) prices in advance for the furnishing of a product or service. This is in direct contrast with the concept of *reimbursement*, in which the service or product is provided first, and then the provider is paid whatever it cost. The *prospective payment system (PPS)* adopted for Medicare, and applied also for other payers, is the most widespread example of prospective pricing.

The first step in prospective pricing is the definition of the product or service for which the price is to be set. Thus the *diagnosis related group (DRG)* system of *classification (1)* of patients, used in the PPS, is the first step in that prospective pricing application. The definition of *procedure*s in

Physicians' Current Procedural Terminology (CPT) could be a first step toward prospective pricing for physician services. Prospective pricing facilitates budgeting on the part of payers, since only the units of service or product likely to be needed have to be estimated or predicted; the cost of each unit is fixed in advance. On the other hand, prospective pricing increases the budgeting problems of the provider, since the provider is now at risk (see *risk (2)*) and must plan much more carefully or else lose on the prospectively priced "transaction" (of course, the provider may also gain on the transaction).

prospective pricing system (PPS): A sometimes translation of "PPS," which is generally translated to mean *"prospective payment system."* "Prospective pricing system" is, however, a more appropriate description of this payment system. See *prospective pricing*.

prospective reimbursement: See *reimbursement*.

provider: A hospital or other health care institution or health care professional which provides health care services to patients. A "provider" may be a single hospital, an individual, or a group or organization.

provider-driven system: See *economic system*.

Provider Reimbursement Review Board (PRRB): A panel of five members appointed by the Secretary of the *Department of Health and Human Services (DHHS)*, to which a *provider* may appeal a decision of a *fiscal intermediary* denying payment for services under Medicare.

PRRB: See *Provider Reimbursement Review Board*.

PSDA: See *Patient Self-Determination Act*.

PSRO: See *Professional Standards Review Organization*.

public advantage certificate: See *certificate of public advantage*.

public health: The organized efforts on the part of society to reduce disease and premature death, and the disability and discomfort produced by disease and other factors, such as injury or environmental hazards.

Public Health Service (PHS): The organization within the *Department of Health and Human Services (DHHS)* which administers the following agencies:

Agency for Toxic Substances and Disease Registry
Alcohol, Drug Abuse, and Mental Health Administration
Centers for Disease Control
Food and Drug Administration
Health Resources and Services Administration
National Center for Health Services Research and
  Health Care Technology Assessment
National Center for Health Statistics
National Center for Toxicological Research
National Institutes of Health
Office of Disease Prevention and Health Promotion
Office of Health Communications

Office of Health Operations
Office of Health Planning and Evaluation
Office of Population Affairs
Office of the Surgeon General of the United States

purchasing group: See *individual and small employer purchasing group*.

Q

QALY: See *quality-adjusted life-year*.

QC: See *quality control*.

QCHP: See *qualified community health plan*.

QCPN: See *qualified community practice network*.

QI: See *quality improvement*.

QIP: See *quality improvement project*.

QM: See *quality management*.

QOL: See *quality of life*.

QRM: See *quality and resource management*.

qualified actuary: Under *HR 3080*, " . . . an individual who is a member of the American Academy of Actuaries (AAA) or meets such reasonable standards and qualifications as the Secretary of Health and Human Services may provide by regulation."

qualified community health plan (QCHP): Under the *Health Security Act (HSA)*, a health plan which is a public or nonprofit private entity whose principal purpose is, with respect to the comprehensive benefit package (CBP), to provide each of such items and services in one or more health professional shortage areas or to a significant number of individuals who are members of a medically underserved population. The QCHP must also be a participant in one or more health alliances, and two or more of the *relevant categories of entities* are among the entities providing health services through the health plan.

qualified community practice network (QCPN): Under the *Health Security Act (HSA)*, a consortium of health care providers which (1) is a public or nonprofit private entity whose principal purpose is to, with respect to the *comprehensive benefit package (CBP)*, to provide each of such items and services in one or more health professional shortage areas or to a significant number of individuals who are members of a medically underserved population; (2) has an agreement with one or more health plans that are participating in one or more health alliances; (3) is governed by a written agreement to which each of the participating providers is a party; and has

(4) two or more of the *relevant categories of entities* represented in the consortium.

qualified health insurance premiums: Under *S 1743*, " . . . premiums for 1) a federally qualified health insurance plan, and 2) any other benefits or plans supplementary to such a federally qualified health insurance plan.

qualified health service area: Under *HR 3080*, " . . . a geographic area that (A) is a rational area for the delivery of health services; (B) has a population of not more than 500,000 individuals; and (C)(i) has been designated by the Secretary [of Health and Human Services] as an area with a shortage of personal health services; or (ii) has a significant number of individuals who have low incomes or who have insufficient insurance regarding health care."

quality-adjusted life-year (QALY): A measure proposed to be used in economic analyses of the benefits of various procedures and programs.

quality and resource management (QRM): A term being used in some hospitals to indicate that *quality management* and the conservation of resources are seen as a single topic, or at least, topics which are closely interrelated. Such hospitals may have, for example, quality management, *utilization review* (see *review*), risk management, and infection control under the "QRM department" headed by the "QRM Director."

quality assurance activities, State medical: See *State medical quality assurance activities.*

quality assurance, internal: See *internal quality assurance* and *internal quality assurance program.*

quality control (QC): The sum of all the activities which prevent unwanted change in quality. In the health care setting, quality control requires a repeated series of feedback loops which monitor and evaluate the care of the individual patient (and other systems in the health care process). These feedback loops involve checking the care being delivered against standards of care (see *standard of care (1)*), the identification of any problems or opportunities for improvement, and prompt corrective action, so that the quality is maintained. The illustration on page 124 shows this feedback loop and also the effect of the entire quality control process (a great many ongoing feedback loops) in maintaining the "quality floor." See also *quality improvement* and *quality management.*

quality function: The sum of all the activities, wherever performed, through which the hospital achieves the *quality of care* it provides. This usage is comparable to speaking of the "fiscal function," which is the sum of the activities, wherever performed, through which the hospital achieves fiscal soundness. The term "quality function" is replacing "quality assurance function."

quality improvement (QI): The sum of all the activities which create desired change in quality. In the health care setting, quality improvement requires a feedback loop which involves the identification of patterns of the care of patients (or of the performance of other systems involved in care), the analysis of those patterns in order to identify opportunities for improvement (or instances of departure from standards of care (see *standard of care (1)*), and then action to improve the quality of care for future patients. An effective quality improvement system results in stepwise increases in quality of care. The illustration on page 124 shows both the feedback loop and the "*quality staircase*."

Quality control, with which quality improvement is sometimes confused, is the sum of all the activities which prevent unwanted change in quality; see *quality management*. See also *quality improvement project*.

continuous quality improvement (CQI): As used in health care today, CQI means the application of industrial *quality management* theory in the health care setting, based upon principles of quality "gurus" W. Edwards Deming and Joseph M. Juran. While traditional "quality control" theories seek out "fault" and attempt improvement by exhorting people to change their behavior, continuous improvement seeks to understand processes and revise them on the basis of data about the processes themselves. CQI sees "problems" as opportunities for improvement. The CQI process involves a project-by-project approach to systematically improve quality, not just to maintain the status quo. A major project in this area is the National Demonstration Project on Quality Improvement in Health Care, sponsored by a grant from the John A. Hartford Foundation, being conducted by Harvard Community Health Plan in Brookline, Massachusetts, in conjunction with the Juran Institute (a quality consulting and education firm in Wilton, Connecticut). See also *quality improvement project (QIP)* and *total quality management (TQM)*.

quality improvement project (QIP): One activity in the process of *continuous quality improvement (CQI)*. Each project involves a process which has been identified as deserving improvement, and which has been given priority (prioritizing of effort is critical in CQI). For each project, a team is assigned. For a project which involves a single department, only members of that department need be involved. When more than one department is involved, the team is called a "cross-functional" team, and consists of representatives from all departments involved in the process targeted for improvement, along with support from senior management. The team studies the process, comes up with theories for improvement, tests the theories, puts successful theories into place, and also puts into place measures to assure that the improved quality is maintained.

Examples of hospital QIPs conducted as part of the the National Demonstration Project on Quality Improvement in Health Care are reduction in medication errors; reduction of unbilled drugs (thereby increasing revenues); reduction of delays in surgery starting times (with a corresponding savings in hospital staff overtime expenses). See also *quality management* and *total quality management (TQM)*.

quality management (QM): A term replacing "quality assurance." Quality management includes the efforts to determine the *quality of care*, to develop and maintain programs to keep it at an acceptable level (*quality control*), to institute improvements when the opportunity arises or the care does not meet standards (*quality improvement*), and to provide, to all concerned, the evidence required to establish confidence that quality is being managed and maintained at the desired level. (These are the same elements that are inherent in industrial quality management.) The advantages of the term "quality management" over "quality assurance" are: (1) there is no implication of a "guarantee," an idea which may be suggested by the use of the word "assurance," which is sometimes used as a synonym for "insurance"; and (2) "quality management" is more accurate, since the achievement of quality depends on people carrying out their responsibilities without error, and getting people to perform is the task of management.

total quality management (TQM): Used to describe the philosphy (and actions) of an organization which is dedicated to *continuous quality improvement (CQI)* throughout the organization. A hospital with total quality management will, for example, set specific quality goals, choose a number of high priority *quality improvement projects* (QIPs), make quality improvement part of job descriptions throughout the organization and legitimize time spent on quality improvement, provide necessary resources (financial and otherwise), provide essential training for staff involved, and formally recognize quality improvement efforts. Total quality management requires commitment and personal involvement of senior management. It should be emphasized that *quality control* (prevention of unwanted change in quality) must be maintained in parallel with quality improvement, and that quality control demands the same energy commitment as does *quality improvement*.

quality of care: The degree of conformity with accepted principles and practices (standards), the degree of fitness for the patient's needs, and the degree of attainment of achievable outcomes (results), consonant with the appropriate allocation or use of resources. The phrase "quality of care" carries the concept that quality is not equivalent to "more" or "higher technology" or higher cost. The "degree of conformity" with standards focuses on the provider's performance, while the "degree of fitness" for the patient's needs indicates that the patient may present conditions which override strict conformity with otherwise prescribed procedures.

quality of life (QOL): A condition often given as one attribute or dimension of health. It is ill-defined, depending on the individual and his or her goals, the social setting and expectations (often of others), and other factors. The goal of much of health care is stated to be improved quality of life. One of the most challenging problems in health care is to measure quality of life so that (1) improvement can be identified, and (2) it can be used as a factor in *cost-benefit analysis*. There is a real danger that inability to express quality of life in numerical terms will mean that much valuable care will not be available because quality of life cannot be given a value and therefore cannot be used to justify the expenditure (to end up with a positive *cost-benefit ratio* rather than a negative ratio); consequently, mere survival could be the measure.

An illustration is the debate over the "value" of some coronary bypass operations; patients in some studies have not shown significantly greater life expectancies with the operation than without it, but the patients operated on regularly testify to their pleasure with their relief from pain.

Quality Control
The Quality <u>Floor</u>: Preventing unwanted change for today's patient

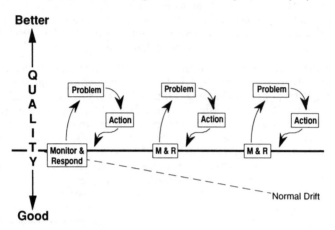

Quality Improvement
The Quality <u>Staircase</u>: Creating desired change for future patients

In some instances (intractable pain or helplessness, for example), life itself is of such low quality to the individual that he may prefer not to live.

health-related quality of life (HRQOL): A number of aspects of quality of life (QOL) which are related to health, such as mental health, perceived physical health, and social functioning. The relevant aspects are sometimes developed under the headings of "physical well-being, perceived health, emotional well-being, home management, work functioning, recreation, social functioning, and sexual functioning."

quality staircase: A method of representing the results of quality improvement efforts. Joseph M. Juran in the industrial setting has represented quality improvement as an ever-rising spiral, an inclined plane. The processes involved in making the product or providing the service are constantly monitored and, as opportunities for improvement are identified, changes are made which result in breakthroughs to higher levels of quality. In certain respects, the concept of a staircase is more appropriate than that of a spiral, since breakthroughs actually improve quality in steps rather than in a continuous fashion. See the illustration on page 124.

quill pen law: A law which requires records to be maintained in written, rather than electronic, form.

R

rate: A financial term referring to a hospital or other institution's *charges*. Typically rates are "fixed" in that they are for specified services (see *service*), and the same rate is charged to all individuals or to purchasers of a given class (such as Medicare patients). For example, a hotel could have different rates for senior citizens, commercial travellers, and the general public.

blended rate: A term used in the *prospective payment system (PPS)* of Medicare to designate a rate which is formed by combining the hospital-specific rate and the federal Medicare rate.

hospital-specific rate: A term used in the Medicare *prospective payment system (PPS)* in the computation of the hospital's payment. This rate is "blended" with the federal Medicare rate in certain circumstances.

inclusive rate: A prospectively established rate for a day of care which includes all hospital services (see *service*) that may be required, regardless of their nature or cost.

interim rate: A temporary rate used in a reimbursement system which periodically makes payments to the hospital on the basis of an estimated figure. The rate is subsequently adjusted retrospectively to reflect actual expenses: additional payments are made to the hospital, or the hospital refunds part of the payment it received; and corrections are made to future rates as appropriate. Using an interim rate provides operating cash for the hospital in a "retrospective reimbursement" payment system, where payment is based on actual costs as determined at the end of the fiscal period.

per diem rate: A rate established by dividing total costs (plus a percentage for excess of income over expenses) by the total number of inpatient days of care for the same period. Thus the per diem rate is the same for each patient, regardless of the patient's illness, its severity, or the diagnostic or therapeutic measures required.

room rate: Same as "daily service charge": the dollar amount the hospital charges for one day of inpatient care for "room and board" and basic nursing and hospital care. The term is not used when, for example, an *inclusive rate* system is employed since, in that case, the daily rate includes more than these items.

rural rate: A type of rate computed by Medicare for hospitals Medicare classifies as rural.

urban rate: A type of rate computed by Medicare for hospitals Medicare classifies as urban.

rate setting: A process of regulation of hospital charges (see *rate*) by an external agency which sets the rates for the institution.

rating: The determination, by an actuary, of the health care *risk (1)* for a given group in order to establish the insurance premium to be charged.

community rating: Establishment of insurance or health care plan premiums on the basis of the average health care demands of an entire community, so that all individuals in the community pay the same premium. The alternative, called *experience rating*, calls for lower premiums for healthier subsets of the population and higher for subsets, such as the elderly, who require more care. Community rating is likely to be mandated under health care reform.

experience rating: Establishment of insurance or health care plan premiums on the basis of an actuarial analysis of the sex and age composition of the group, type of industry, and other factors, which are used to set the initial premiums. In subsequent years, the actual record of the group may be used to modify the rating and the premiums. Often preexisting conditions are taken into the analysis and may be cause for rejection of enrollment of certain individuals. Actuarial analyses would, for example, give weights to sex and age: A preponderance of young males would point to a lower rate than females because of the lower obstetric exposure, but this would be countered by the higher accidental injury rates for males. Actuarial analysis is a complicated science. Experience rating is, of course, sought by employers of young, healthy individuals. The result is that the remainder of a given population, with poorer experience, pays more.

Community rating, on the other hand, forbids experience rating, and averages the premiums across the entire population.

rating band: The range of difference in insurance premiums for a specific class of individuals. Some health care reform proposals require that such bands be eliminated, that is, they require that all insurers adopt the same rate for a given class of individuals.

ratio of costs to charges (RCC): A method of estimating costs in accounting. There is generally a desire that charges for health care reflect the costs of that care. This is fairly easy to achieve globally, that is, the total costs for a hospital, say, for a year can be ascertained and the charges or reimbursement can be matched to those costs. It is also easy to learn the total costs and the total charges for a revenue producing department, such as radiology. Typically, the total charges exceed the total costs, and the ratio between these two figures is easily obtained.

Since it may be virtually impossible (or far more costly than can be justified) to find the actual costs of specific *procedures* and *services*, such as the cost of a chest X-ray, an approximation is made. Under the RCC approach, this is done by simply multiplying the charge for the procedure by the cost/charge ratio for the department, and using the resulting dollar amount as (an estimate of) the cost of the procedure. For example, if the (total) costs for the department are $100,000 and the (total) charges are $200,000, the ratio, $100,000/$200,000, is 0.5. Applying the RCC method, then, all charges would be multiplied by this ratio, and a chest X-ray, say, for which there is a $50.00 charge would be considered to have a $25.00 cost.

rationing: A process of withholding goods or services when they are in short supply. Rationing of health care is, of course, in one sense in effect, since it is not possible to provide all the care which has been proven effective to all the individuals who might benefit from it. In the climate of health care reform, discussion revolves around the problems of deciding the basis on which the limited financial and other resources will be allocated; on who will get what care there is. One method of rationing is financial: when the money runs out the care stops. This is first-come first-served. Another rationing method is to identify certain groups of patients, such as Medicare and Medicaid, as eligible for the benefits. Other methods have been proposed, such as cutting benefits off on the basis of age. Perhaps the most scientific and fair method proposed is the "Oregon plan" in which there is an *explicit* list of patient-care "problem-treatment (diagnosis-treatment) pairs," ranked as to their benefits to the individuals and to society. Those most beneficial, ranked highest, are funded first, and actuarial methods determine how far down the list the available funds will go. A line is drawn at that point, and lower ranked services are not paid for from the given fund source. See *Oregon plan*.

RBRVS: See *resource-based relative value scale* under *relative value scale*.

REACH: See *rural emergency access care hospital*.

readmission: A second (or later) *admission* of a patient to a facility. Sometimes the term is used in a manner that implies that the readmission is for further treatment for the condition occasioning the previous admission, because of recurrence of the problem or failure of completion of care; however, this inference is not warranted.

rebuttable presumption: A fact which shifts the "burden of proof" from one party to the other in a lawsuit. It has been proposed that if a physician sued for malpractice has followed approved clinical practice guidelines (see *guidelines (2)*), this would create a legal presumption that the physician was not negligent. Such a presumption may be rebutted by the plaintiff offering additional evidence, but it will be harder for the plaintiff to win in such a case.

recoding: Placing data (cases, for example) from one *classification (1)* into categories of a second classification (when there is one-to-one correspondence) or by concatenating one or more categories from the first classification into the second, a sort of "compound grouping." Where the groups of the second classification are more specific than or different from those of the first classification, recoding should not be attempted, because no exact recoding is possible; data once coded to a category cannot be "split" without going back to more detailed sources. See *coding*.

recuse: To reject or challenge an individual's qualification to serve in a given capacity, usually on the basis of conflict of interest or known bias. Usually used with respect to a judge or juror. Individuals may also recuse themselves voluntarily, to avoid the appearance of impropriety.

redlining: See *blacklisting*.

regional alliance, regional health alliance: See *health alliance*.

regional professional foundation (RPF): Under the *Health Security Act (HSA)*, a regional organization, established and overseen by the *National Health Board (NHB)*, including at least one academic health center, with responsibility for "1) developing programs for lifetime learning for health professionals . . . ; 2) fostering collaboration among health plans and health care providers to improve the quality of primary and specialized care; 3) disseminating information about quality improvement programs, practice guidelines, and research findings; 4) disseminate information on innovative uses of health professionals; 5) developing innovative patient education systems that enhance patient involvement in decisions relating to their health care; and 6) applying for and conducting research . . . "

regulation: A rule or procedure made by a governmental *agency*, and having the force of law, as contrasted with an *administrative guideline* (see *guidelines (1)*), which is merely advisory.

　　Another type of regulation is that adopted by a corporation or association as part of its internal rules and regulations. However, this latter type of regulation is seldom spoken of separate from the phrase, "rules and regulations" of the corporation.

reimbursement: The payment to a hospital or other *provider*, after the fact, of an amount equal to the provider's expenses in providing a given service or product. The current trend is away from such a "blank check" approach and toward *prospective pricing*, that is, toward agreement in advance as to the amount which will be paid for the service or product in question. Several varieties of reimbursement are discussed in health care:

cost-based reimbursement: Payment of all *allowable costs* (see *cost*) incurred in the provision of care. The term "allowable" refers to the terms of the contract under which care is furnished.

prospective reimbursement: A term sometimes used, incorrectly, instead of *prospective pricing* or *prospective payment*. See *prospective payment system (PPS)*. Also, "prospective reimbursement" is sometimes used to describe the prospectively estimated amount to be paid a hospital on a current schedule so that it will have operating cash, with the understanding that adjustments will be made later in the light of actual operating cost data. The concept is similar to that of the *periodic interim payment (PIP)*.

retroactive reimbursement: Additional payment to a provider for costs not considered at the time of original reimbursement.

retrospective reimbursement: Payment based on actual costs as determined at the end of the fiscal period.

third party reimbursement (TPR): Payment for health care services by a *third party* such as an insurance company. See *third party payer* under *payer*.

reimbursement specialist (1): A person who prepares the statements and other materials needed to obtain reimbursement from *third-party payers* (see *payer*) and insurers for *services*, and who maintains the related records. Synonym(s): insurance clerk.

reimbursement specialist (2): A person who is involved with working out the terms and details of *reimbursement* systems with *third-party payers* (see *payer*).

reinsurance: A type of insurance that insurance companies themselves buy for their own protection. Reinsurance further shares the risk. Health care insurances frequently reinsure themselves for specified, rare, and high priced risks, such as heart transplantation.

relative value scale (RVS): A numerical system (scale) designed to permit comparisons of the resources needed (or appropriate prices) for various units of service. The RVS is the compiled table of the *relative value units* (RVUs) for all the objects in the class for which it is developed.

An RVS takes into account labor, skill, supplies, equipment, space, and other costs into an aggregate cost for each *procedure* or other unit of *service*. The aggregate cost is converted into the *relative value unit (RVU)* of the procedure or service by relating it to the cost of a procedure or service selected as the "base unit." For example, the developer of the RVS for laboratory work might decide to use the cost of a red blood count as the base unit. Its actual cost might be $5.00, but, as the base, its RVU would arbitrarily be set at 1.0. If a blood sugar estimation, then, actually cost $25.00, it would have an RVU value of 5.0 ($25.00 divided by $5.00) (the illustration is imaginary as to the prices given). If a urinalysis cost $3.00, it would have an RVU of 0.6.

In a payment system based on the RVS, payment is determined by a formula which multiplies the RVU by a dollar amount called a "converter" (see *conversion factor*).

resource-based relative value scale (RBRVS): A method of determining physicians' *fees* based on the time, training, skill, and other factors required to deliver various *services*. The term came into use in 1988 upon release of the report of a study commissioned by the *Department of Health and Human Services (DHHS)* and carried out under the direction of Harvard economist William Hsiao, PhD. See *relative value scale* and also *behavior offset*.

relative value unit (RVU): The numerical value given to each *procedure* or other unit of *service* in a "relative value scale." See *relative value scale (RVS)*.

relevant categories of entities: Under the *Health Security Act (HSA)*, categories of entities two of which must be represented in community health plans or community health networks for these plans or networks to be deemed "qualified." The categories, listed in Sec. 3421(d), are, in general, entities providing services under public health or other specified federal or state programs.

report card: An element of the health care reform proposals that is designed to inform patients and health care buyers of doctor and hospital performance and of patient satisfaction.

consumer report card: One promised element of the *Health Security Act (HSA)*. It appears to be a report *to* consumers on the performance of doctors and hospitals so that ". . . they are held accountable based on results . . ."

Resource Mothers Development Project (RMDP): See *National Commission to Prevent Infant Mortality*.

resource utilization groups (RUGs): A *case mix* payment system used in New York state for *long-term care* patients under Medicare and Medicaid.

respite care: Short term care (usually a few days) for a *long-term care* patient in order to provide a respite (rest and change) for those who have been caring for the patient, usually the patient's family. Respite care may involve hospitalization of the patient, or provision of round-the-clock care at home or in a nursing home as needed.

responsible party: The individual or organization responsible for placing a patient in a health care facility and ensuring that adequate care is given to that patient there. For example, a parent is usually the responsible party in the case of a child; the parent is not only responsible for the child receiving care, but also for the payment for that care. In less formal usage in the hospital, the term "responsible party" is used to mean simply "responsible for payment." Legally, there can be more than one "responsible party." For example, one person, such as a guardian, may be authorized to make treatment decisions, while another person may be responsible for payment.

rest home care: Care for a patient who is unable to live independently, that is, who needs assistance with the activities of daily living (ADL), and who may need occasional assistance from a professional nurse. Such professional nursing service is obtained from a visiting nurse. The setting for rest home care (formerly called custodial care) is, understandably, a rest home.

review: There are many kinds of review carried out in health care; all are processes of evaluation. Some relevant to health care reform discussion:

admissions review: An evaluation of the appropriateness of the *admission* of the patient to the hospital. The admissions review determines whether the patient in question was in a condition which warranted use of the hospital, or could (or should) have been treated in some other setting (for example, at home or as an outpatient, or in a hospital more suited to managing the patient's problem). Typically, the admissions review is carried out at or shortly after admission.

capital expenditure review (CER): A process carried out by a state agency prior to granting permission to the hospital to incur a capital expenditure.

claims review: Retrospective review of hospital claims (see *claim*) by a *third party payer* (see *payer*) in order to determine the: (1) liability of the payer (whether the benefit was included in the contract); (2) eligibility of the *beneficiary* and the *provider*; (3) appropriateness of the *service*; and (4) appropriateness of the amount claimed.

concurrent review: Evaluation of medical necessity for *admission* and *appropriateness* of services, carried out while the patient is in the hospital (concurrent with the care). The advantage of concurrent review is that if any action (change in the care) is found to be necessary as a finding of the review, it can be taken while the patient is still in the hospital.

external independent review: Under *HR 3704*, such review is required of a risk contracting entity to be " . . . conducted by a utilization control and peer review organization . . . or another organization unaffiliated with the State government or with any risk contracting entity and approved by the Secretary [of Health and Human Services]." The requirement may be deemed in compliance if the review is carried out by an *accrediting organization* meeting the requirements of the Act.

medical services review: *Retrospective review* of the use of services (and failure to use services), for both *inpatient*s and *outpatient*s, with respect to the medical *appropriateness* of the services and, in some situations, review of whether the services are included in the patient's insurance *benefits*.

preadmission review: Evaluation, prior to *admission*, of the necessity for *elective* hospitalization for the individual patient in question.

preprocedure review: A review of a case prior to the performance of a given *procedure* in order to determine (1) if the procedure is medically indicated, and (2) if the procedure could equally well be performed in an alternate setting.

private review: *Utilization review* performed on patients whose care is paid for by private sources (sources other than government).

prospective review (1): A term sometimes used to refer to evaluation of a patient's need for hospitalization prior to admission. "*Preadmission review*" is a better term for this meaning.

prospective review (2): A term now being applied to a review of the planning for a patient's future treatment, site of care (home, hospital, and so on) and other details.

rate review: Review by a regulatory *agency* of a hospital's budget and financial picture in order to determine the reasonableness of the hospital's proposed rates and rate changes. Rate review is also applied to rates for certain *prepayment plans*, such as *Blue Cross/Blue Shield (BC/BS)*, depending on state laws.

retrospective review: Review after the fact. The term most often refers to a "patient care audit" (see *medical care evaluation*).

utilization review (UR): The examination and evaluation of the *efficiency* and *appropriateness* of any health care service. Often the term applies to a concurrent process, one carried out during hospitalization, for determination of the individual patient's need for continued stay.

right to die: The legal right to refuse life-saving or life-sustaining treatment. A competent adult has the legal right to refuse medical treatment, even if that treatment is essential to sustain life. Some refer to this right as the "right to die." The issue of the "right to die" arises in the situation where a person has a condition in which the *quality of life* is so intolerable that death, at least in the belief of that individual (or those responsible for that person), is preferable. If the person is conscious (and mentally competent), she may exercise the right to refuse treatment for herself; but if she is unconscious or otherwise incompetent, others must make the decision for her. Serious legal and ethical issues are involved in the latter case. See *advance directives*.

risk (1): An actuary's statement of the risk presented by a group of individuals which is being considered for enrollment in health care insurance. This risk statement is the basis for rating the group, i.e., determining the insurance premium to be charged. For *community rating*, the risk statement is for the entire community; for *experience rating*, the statement is for a smaller group, such as the employees of a given corporation. See *rating*.

risk (2): *Health care plan* risk. A term which, when used in connection with organizations for providing patient care, refers to finances. For example, a *health maintenance organization (HMO)* which offers prepaid care for a given fee or premium is "at risk"; that is, it must provide the care within the premium funds available or find the money elsewhere (the individual assets of the partners, for example). See also *risk pool*.

risk-adjustment factors: Under *HR 3222*, factors used in the adjustment of premiums for various types of enrollment, taking into account increased or diminished risk for consumption of the services included in the uniform set of effective benefits for individual enrollee units; the same single factor would be applied to all covered individuals in the unit.

risk contracting entity: Under *HR 3704*, " . . . an entity which has a contract with a State agency . . . under which the entity A) provides or arranges for the provision of health care items or services which are specified in such contract . . . ; and B) is at risk . . . for part or all of the cost of such items or services . . . "

Under *HR 3080,* an entity which has a contract with a State agency under which the entity is at risk for part or all of the cost of the care rendered.

risk management program: Under *HR 3080,* a program "to prevent and provide early warning of practices which may result in injuries to patients or which otherwise may endanger patient safety." States must require each insurer to establish risk management programs or sanction such programs provided by other entities, and the State must require each professional and provider to participate in one such program at least once in each 3-year period.

risk pool: A fund set up as a reserve for unexpected expenses in a *prepaid health plan.* Organizations which provide prepaid health care for a fixed fee typically set up such pools to cover, for example, unusually large demands for hospital care or specialist services. See *risk (2).*

high risk pool: A fund set up to offer health insurance to small groups and individuals who have been denied coverage or whose medical history makes rates too high. See *risk (1).*

risk pooling: Under *HR 3080,* a method of collecting "excess" money from insurers with below average health risks and putting that money in a common fund for payment to insurers with above average health risks, both collection and payment "in relation to the degree of their favorable or adverse risk selection."

risk selection: Action by a health care plan or insurer which seeks to enroll only healthy persons (low *risk (1)),* thus reducing the risk to the plan. Of course, adverse risk selection (see *adverse selection)* results in enrollment of a group of persons who are below the norm in health, and thus likely to be more costly for the plan. Health care reform proposals would, along with requiring *community rating* (see *rating),* prevent risk selection.

RMDP: Resource Mothers Development Project. See *National Commission to Prevent Infant Mortality.*

Rowland bill: See *HR 3573.*

RPF: See *regional professional foundation.*

RUGs: See *resource utilization groups.*

rural emergency access care hospital (REACH): Under *HR 3080,* special provisions are made for " . . . a facility which the Secretary [of Health and Human Services] . . . " finds meets a number of requirements spelled out in the Act. Among these provisions, there must be "a practitioner who is qualified to provide advanced cardiac life support services . . . on site at the facility on a 24-hour basis . . . and a physician is on call to provide emergency medical services on a 24-hour basis . . . " Such a facility does not, however, need to meet otherwise hospital standards relating to the number of hours a day or days a week in which the facility must be open.

rural emergency access care hospital services: Under *HR 3080,* " . . . medical and other health services furnished by a *rural emergency access care hospital.*"

rural health network: Under *HR 3704*, " . . . a formal cooperative agreement between participating hospitals, physicians, and other health care providers which A) furnishes health care services to medicare beneficiaries; B) is located in a rural area; and C) is governed by a board of directors selected by participating health care providers."

rural practice agreement: Under *HR 3704*, a written agreement by a physician or a registered nurse, nurse practitioner, or physician's assistant under which, in return for a qualified educational loan, the individual agrees to perform full-time services as such a medical professional for a period of months.   When the period is 24 months, the agreement is termed "qualified."

RVS: See *relative value scale*.

RVU: See *relative value unit*.

S

S 1579:   "Breaux bill."   Also called "Managed Competition Act of 1993" (introduced in the House by the "Cooper-Grandy bill," HR 3222).

S 1743:   "Nickels bill."   Introduced by Senator Nickels on 20 November 1993.   The emphasis is on portable health insurance benefits and greater choice of health insurance plans.   Also called the "Consumer Choice Health Security Act of 1993."

S 1757:   "Mitchell bill."   See *Health Security Act (HSA)*.

S 1770:   "Chafee bill."   Also called "Health Equity and Access Reform Today Act of 1993" (introduced in the House by the "Thomas bill," HR 3704).

S 1775:   "Moynihan bill."   See *Health Security Act (HSA)*.

S 1779:   "Kennedy bill."   See *Health Security Act (HSA)*.

safe harbor regulations: *Regulations* which describe certain acts or behaviors which will *not* be illegal under a specific law, even though they might overwise arguably be illegal.   Recently, the term has been applied to proposed *Department of Health and Human Services (DHHS)* regulations which would provide a "safe harbor" for certain joint ventures and other arrangements between hospitals and physicians or among physicians, so that these activities would not violate federal Medicare *fraud and abuse* laws.

SEC: See *Securities and Exchange Commission*.

secondary care: Specialized care provided by a physician or hospital, usually on referral from a primary care physician.   Synonym(s): specialized care.

Section 1122: A section of the Social Security Act which denies payment for certain capital expenditures not approved by state planning agencies.

Securities and Exchange Commission (SEC): An independent federal agency after which the *Jackson Hole Group* has modeled its proposed *National Health Board (NHB)*.

self-care: Those activities that individuals initiate and perform for themselves in connection with their health and well-being.

self-pay patient: See *self-responsible patient*.

self-regulatory entity: See *medical self-regulatory entity*.

self-responsible patient: A patient who pays either all or part of the hospital bill from his or her own resources, as opposed to third-party payment (payment by an insurance company, Medicare, or Blue Cross/Blue Shield (BC/BS)), for example). Synonym(s): self-pay patient.

Senior Plan Network (SPN): An alliance of *health maintenance organizations* (HMOs) which offers enrollment in the SPN, and thus in its constituent HMOs. Medicare prepays part or all the cost of enrollment in an SPN as it does in an HMO under certain circumstances.

separation: A term used in Canada to mean the same as patient "*discharge*" in the U.S. It is the formal release of a patient from a hospital (or other care).

service: The term "service" has many meanings in health care, and must be examined in context. In health care financing, service means something "done" for a patient by a physician or other person. The term often occurs in the phrase "procedures and services," and it is sometimes difficult if not impossible to distinguish the two; a specific act might equally well be called a "procedure" or a "service." Generally, procedures tend to be distinct actions, and are carried out in a brief time, as, for example, a surgical operation (a procedure or group of surgical procedures done at one time). On the other hand, services (such as the preoperative and postoperative care for the same operation) are less distinct and are carried out over longer (and variable) periods of time.

In health care financing, the physician's "initial hospital care" of a patient is called a "service," although it is largely limited (in billing for care) to what is done upon admission of the patient; each subsequent day's care is defined as another "service." However, the "50-minute hour" in the psychiatrist's office for "medical psychotherapy" is listed in *Physician's Current Procedural Terminology, 4th Edition (CPT-4)*, as a "procedure."

For purposes of health care financing, a "service" (or procedure) might more accurately be defined as "the unit for which a *charge* is made." See also *procedure*.

cognitive services: A term applied to all the activities of a physician (or other professional) other than the performance of *procedures*. The charges of physicians are relatively easy to explain in surgery and other instances where "something is done" to the patient. High charges for, say, diagnostic evaluations, patient and family counseling, and the care of patients with infectious diseases, are much harder to explain, and thus charges are considerably lower. "Cognitive services" require as much time and skill as surgery. However, much of this effort and skill is simply not seen by the patient or payer. Nonetheless, an education as long and arduous as the surgeon's may be required, as well as unseen time in the library and informal consultation with colleagues. Efforts to overcome the resulting perceived inequities in payment have led to the labeling of non-procedural services as cognitive (intellectual). No term for "non-cognitive" services seems to have appeared.

service benefits: See *benefits.*

severity of illness: The gravity of a patient's condition. Patients with the same diagnosis often vary from being mildly ill to being extremely ill, or even dying. Under the *prospective payment system (PPS)*, every patient with the same diagnosis (actually, every patient within a given *diagnosis related group (DRG)*, of which there are only 468) is given the same "price tag." No allowance is made for the severity of the patient's illness. Efforts are underway to persuade the federal government to make such an allowance, and other efforts are being made to develop practical methods for quantifying "severity of illness" so that it can be reliably incorporated in the mathematics of the pricing formula. Such quantification is referred to as developing a "severity index" or "score." The stimulus for severity measures is illustrated, for example, by the fact that a diabetic patient in coma (very severely ill) understandably should cost more to treat than one hospitalized simply to "fine-tune" the control of the diabetes. Note that a measure of severity on admission to the hospital, followed by another later measure, permits evaluation of the patient's progress under care, while a measure which can only show severity on discharge does not permit this interpretation.

Several systems are now in development or use in hospitals: Apache II, disease staging, patient management categories (PMCs), computerized severity index (CSI), personal computer stager (PC-stager), and Medis-Groups.

shadow pricing: Setting the price for a product by matching the price for the same or similar product to that of a competitor. Some HMOs are said to have failed because they have used this method in establishing their premiums rather than actuarial analysis, in which the premium is set by defining a specific benefit package to be provided to a population whose demographic characteristics are carefully considered.

shamrock organization: See *virtual organization.*

SHCC: See *statewide health coordinating council.*

S/HMO: See *social/health maintenance organization* under *health maintenance organization.*

sin tax: A tax on products or activities which are allegedly harmful; for example, alchohol and cigarettes.

single-payer plan: A method of health care financing in which there is only one source of money for paying health care providers. The *Canadian-style system* is the prime example of a single-payer plan, but not all elements of the Canadian program need be included for a plan to be "single-payer"; in fact, the single-payer could be an insurance company. Or the scope of the plan would not have to be national; it could be employed by a single state or community. Proponents of a single-payer plan emphasize the administrative simplicity for patients and providers, and the resulting significant savings in cost.

skim: A term which, in hospital usage, usually means to select patients who will be financially profitable (for example, because they have an illness for which the *prospective payment system (PPS)* favors the hospital, or because they have insurance and are not charity patients).

small employer: Under *HR 3080*, " . . . an employer that normally employs more than 1 but less than 51 eligible employees on a typical business day . . . ."employee" includes a self-employed individual . . . " Under *HR 3704*, " . . . with respect to a calendar year, an employer that normally employs 1 or more but less than 101 eligible employees on a typical business day."

small employer pool: The banding together of several small employers in order to compete in purchasing power with large employers. The *health alliance (HA)* being proposed in the 1993 health care reform proposals is a form of such a pool. See *managed competition*.

small group market reform: A subset of the health care reform effort directed at improving the cost and accessibility of health insurance for small employers. See *small group reform*.

small group reform: An approach to health care reform which would regulate insurers who sell policies to small businesses, to make insurance more available and affordable. Such regulations may, for example, outlaw *cherry picking*, *predatory pricing*, *medical underwriting* (see *underwriting (2)*), and other questionable practices.

smart card: A "credit card" type of electronic storage card containing key information about an individual's health status, medical history, health insurance coverage, and so forth. The cards are not yet in widespread use in the U.S.

Social Security Administration (SSA): The division of the federal government which administers Medicare, Medicaid (on the federal level), Social Security Insurance (SSI) pensions, and other programs.

specialized care: See *secondary care*.

specialized center of care: Under *HR 3704*, " . . . an institution or other organized system for the provision of specific services, which need not be multidisciplinary, and does not include (except as the Secretary [of Health and Human Services] may provide) individual practitioners." A service mark may be established by the Secretary for such centers.

spell of illness: A term, used in determining Medicare benefits, which is defined as a period of time starting when the patient enters the hospital and ending at the conclusion of a 60-consecutive-day period during which the patient has not been an inpatient of any hospital or skilled nursing facility (SNF). (The patient's actual illness ordinarily would have started prior to the hospitalization, and might or might not have concluded within the 60-day period outside the hospital.)

spend-down eligibility: A method of determining eligibility for medical assistance which originated with Medicaid. A person may not have income above a certain level to qualify for the assistance (for example, $500 per month). However, a person with an income of $600 may "spend-down" $100 per month for health care, and qualify for assistance for monthly expenses over $100. This is similar to a deductible.

SPN: See *Senior Plan Network*.

sponsor: In the concept of "managed competition," the sponsor is the intermediary between the purchasers of health care and the *accountable health plans* (AHPs). Large employers usually serve as sponsors themselves, while the *health alliance (HA)* is the sponsor for small employers (and people not covered by their employment). See *managed competition*.

SSA: See *Social Security Administration*.

SSI: See *Supplemental Security Income*.

standard: A measure of quality or quantity, established by an authority, by a profession, or by custom, which serves as a criterion for evaluation.

JCAHO standard: A statement, developed by the *Joint Commission on Accreditation of Healthcare Organizations (JCAHO)*, of the requirements which must be met by the institution in question (such as a hospital, mental health facility, or ambulatory care program) if the institution is to meet JCAHO's requirements for accreditation.

standard benefit forms: Under the *Health Security Act (HSA)*, within one year there would be three standard benefit forms: (1) enrollment and disenrollment; (2) clinical encounter form; and (3) claims form.

standard of care (1): The principles and practices which have been accepted by a health care profession as expected to be applied for a patient under ordinary circumstances. Standards of care are developed from a consensus of experts, based on specific research (where such is available) and expert experience. "Under ordinary circumstances" refers to the fact that a given patient may have individual conditions which are overriding; absent such considerations, a medical staff or nursing staff quality review committee will expect the generally accepted principles and practices to be carried out.

For example, the standard of care for a bedfast patient requires the nursing service to carry out certain procedures to minimize the patient's chances of developing bedsores. The standard of care for a patient with a suspected fracture is to X-ray the area; however, severe bleeding may override (for an extended period of time) the standard calling for the X-ray.

In other words, the *first* standard of care is that the individual patient's needs come before the "general" standard. See also *parameter*.

standard of care (2):   The measure to be applied, in a *malpractice* suit, to the actions of the health care professional in order to determine if the professional was negligent (see *professional negligence* under *negligence*). The rule for determining the standard varies from state to state, but it can be generally stated that the standard of care for health care professionals is to exercise that degree of care and skill practiced by other professionals of similar skill and training (and, in some states, in the same geographic locality) under similar circumstances (see *school rule* and *locality rule*).

The legal "standard of care" may or may not be the same as the "general" *standard of care (1)* in a particular case. The jury (or, in some cases, the judge) in a malpractice case decides what the appropriate "degree of care and skill" is in *that* case, based on the facts and upon the expert testimony offered by both the plaintiff and the defendant.   Differences in juries' opinions on the relevant standard of care is one reason why two malpractice cases with similar facts can have different results.

On rare occasions, the legal standard of care may be higher than that of the health care profession.   For example, a 32 year old woman developed glaucoma and suffered permanent eye damage, after her physicians failed to detect the condition while treating her from 1959 until 1968.   Medical experts for both plaintiff (the woman) and defendent ophthalmologists testified that the standards of the ophthalmology profession did not require routine glaucoma testing for patients under 40.   However, the court concluded that since the test was simple, inexpensive, and painless, the standard itself was negligent. *Helling v. Carey*, 83 Wash.2d 514, 519 P.2d 981 (1974).

standard setting and enforcement activities: Under *HR 3080*, 1) "accreditation of health care practitioners, health care providers, medical education institutions, or medical education programs; 2) technology assessment and risk management activities; 3) development and implementation of practice guidelines or practice parameters; or official peer review proceedings undertaken by a hospital medical staff (or committee thereof) or a medical society or association for purposes of evaluating the quality of health care provided by a medical professional."

State health allowance program: Under *HR 3080*, " . . . a program in effect [eventually] in all political subdivisions of the State [with some exceptions] under which the State makes payments to a group health plan [approved] which provides coverage to the individual as an allowance towards the cost of providing the individual with benefits under the plan." At least one of the plans in the State must be capitated. The program would automatically include "Medicaid categorically eligible individuals." In addition, the State may make this program available to any individual who is not offered coverage under an employer group health plan.

state health plan: A statement issued by the *statewide health coordinating council (SHCC)* covering goals and priorities for the health systems within the state and the desired health status of the residents. The state health plan describes the health systems which would result in high quality health services, available and accessible to all residents, and providing continuity of care at reasonable cost.

state health planning and development agency: A state government *agency* required under federal law as a unit in the official planning process. Among its duties are the development of a *state health plan* and the administration of the state's *certificate of need (CON)* program.

State insurance market reform program: Under *HR 3704*, a program to be instituted by each State to: (1) certify insured health plans; (2) establish health care coverage areas (HCCA); (3) develop procedures for establishment of purchasing groups; (4) prepare and disseminate information about qualified health plans and purchasing groups; (5) provide for a risk adjustment program; (6) develop a binding arbitration process; and (7) specify an annual general enrollment period.

state mandate: See *mandate.*

State medical quality assurance activities: Under *HR 3080*, include 1) "licensing and certifying health care professionals and providers . . . ; 2) operating alternative dispute resolution systems (ADR); 3) carrying out public education programs relating to medical malpractice and the availability of ADR systems . . . ; and 4) carrying out programs to reduce malpractice-related costs for retired providers or other providers volunteering to provide services in medically underserved areas."

statewide health coordinating council (SHCC): An organization of health care *providers* and planners required under federal law as a unit in the official planning process. An SHCC concerns itself with where, how large, and what kind of health care facilities are needed and will be permitted.

strategy: A term derived from the military, and which concerns the long-range, large goals of the organization. In traditional thinking, strategy should precede the development of the *tactics* with which it is implemented. A current insight is that a successful strategy can only be developed after the available tactics are assessed and used to their maximum.

structure: In *quality management,* a term referring to the resources and organization of the health care institution. It is commonly stated that three things can be measured in relation to quality: structure, process, and outcome. "Process" refers to the things done. "Outcome" is a somewhat vague term that presumably refers to the results of the process. In various usages "outcome" may refer to survival, *quality of life,* or the outcomes of tests or procedures; it must be defined in a given usage. The Joint Commission on Accreditation of Healthcare Organizations (JCAHO) originally considered only structure on the theory that "given a good nest, good birds will result." More recently, while affirming that it is now "outcome-oriented," JCAHO has also given attention to process in its surveying of health care organizations.

subscriber: As used in health insurance and with prepayment plans, the person who actually has the contract for care. Dependents of the subscriber, as well as the subscriber himself, are all *enrollees*, but not all enrollees are subscribers.

supermed: A term applied to giant, vertically integrated health care firms which some have predicted will appear in the U.S. Such firms are envisioned as national in scope, market-driven (see *market-driven system* under *economic system*), capitalizing on their "brand names," and specializing in contractual services to large nationwide industries. See also *integration*.

Supplemental Security Income (SSI): A federal income support program for low-income aged, blind, and disabled individuals.

T

tactics: A term derived from the military usage concerning actions which, while directed toward the large goal, are smaller in scale or scope than strategic actions. Tactics are those actions through which a "strategy" is carried out. Strategy is long-range, and lays out the nature and sequence of the steps to be taken to achieve the large goals of the organization. In traditional thinking, strategy should precede the development of the tactics with which it is implemented. A current insight is that a successful strategy can only be developed after the available tactics are assessed and used to their maximum.

tailgate pricing: A pejorative term used to describe pricing which the commentator feels simply responds to the demand of the market (competition) at the moment, that is, pricing which is not based on costs or a consistent pricing policy.

Task Force on National Health Reform: The body created by President Clinton in January 1993, chaired by Hillary Rodham Clinton, with the charge to "listen to all parties and prepare health care reform legislation . . ." It reports that in its deliberations it met with health care providers, consumers, business, and labor groups, including physician groups, nurses groups, hospitals, medical colleges, seniors, long-term care groups, groups representing the disability community, groups specializing in mental health issues, women's groups, children's advocacy groups, minority organizations, rural groups, groups representing small and large businesses, and labor organizations.

tax credit: An amount that can be subtracted from the tax owed by an individual. Some health care reform proposals include tax credits. These save the individual more money than would the same amount taken as a *tax deduction*. In some cases, the credit may only reduce the amount of tax owed; in other cases, the credit may actually be refunded to the taxpayer.

tax-deductible: An adjective applied to contributions to *501(c)(3) corporations*. The contribution may be taken as a *tax deduction* by the donor; the term does not refer to the receiving corporation.

tax deduction: An amount which can be subtracted from the taxable income of an individual. Some health care reform proposals include tax deductions as a way to help the individual finance health care. Tax deductions save the individual less money than would the same amount taken as a *tax credit*.

Tax Equity and Fiscal Responsibility Act (TEFRA): A 1982 federal act which, in its provisions pertaining to Medicare and Medicaid, contained provisions limiting hospital costs.

tax-exempt: A *nonprofit* organization which is not required to pay certain federal (and/or state) taxes. A tax-exempt organization may also qualify to receive tax-deductible donations; see *501(c)(3) corporation*.

tax incentive: A method of encouraging behavior by providing favorable tax treatment (exemptions, deductions, or credits). The *Health Security Act (HSA)* proposes several tax incentives: special treatment for long-term care insurance and services; a tax credit for 50% of the cost ($15,000 maximum) of personal care and assistance services for employed individuals with disabilities (see *individual with disability*); and several incentives for providers to encourage primary care services in a *health professional shortage area*.

tax preference for health benefits: The way that federal law treats health benefits for employees. They have been treated as tax-deductible business expenses for the employeer, rather than taxable income to the employee. This practice results in far lower tax revenue for the government, something in the range of $90 billion dollars per year.

TEFRA: See *Tax Equity and Fiscal Responsibility Act.*

telecommunication technologies: Under *HR 3080*, which encourages demonstration programs regarding telecommunications, projects are to be established which " . . . establish telecommunications between rural medical facilities and medical facilities that have expertise or equipment that can be utilized by the rural facilities through the telecommunications . . . " which " . . . telecommunications technologies include interactive video telecommunications, static video imaging transmitted through the telephone system, and facsimiles transmitted through such system."

telemedicine: Medical care provided through telecommunication when the patient and the caregiver are at separate physical locations. Involves application of interactive audio-visual technology in patient care and education of physicians and other health care personnel, as well as the more traditional access to medical and related records.

terminal care: Care for a patient in the terminal stages of his or her illness; care for a dying patient. See also *hospice program*.

tertiary care: Care of a highly technical and specialized nature, provided in a medical center (usually one affiliated with a university), for patients with unusually severe, complex, or uncommon problems. Tertiary care is the highest level of care. @TERM = therapeutic intervention: *Treatment* which includes active measures, as opposed to simply permitting a disease to run its course or an injury to heal.

therapy: *Treatment.* A term which, when used alone, as in "the patient is undergoing therapy," means that the patient is being treated. When used with a modifier, as in "speech therapy," the term means a specific treatment method or technique.

third party: A term used in connection with health care financing. The first and second parties are the patient and the provider. The third party is a *payer* who is neither of these. Examples are Blue Cross and Blue Shield, commercial insurance, and government. Third parties are increasingly employers, who try to save the money paid to insurance companies or other third parties.

third party administrator (TPA): An organization which administers health care *benefits* (and other employee benefits), primarily for corporations which are self-insured. The third party administrator's services include *claims review* (see *review*) and *claims processing*, primarily of medical claims but also dental, disability, workers' compensation, life insurance, and pension claims.

Thomas bill (HR 3704): See *Health Equity and Access Reform Today Act of 1993.*

Title XIX: See *Medicaid.*

Title XVIII: See *Medicare.*

tort: A wrong for which the law provides a civil remedy, and which is not a breach of contract (contracts are covered by a separate body of laws). A person who commits an act which is a tort is legally liable (responsible) to anyone injured by the act. "Civil remedy" means that the person doing the legal "wrong" must pay the victim money to make good her losses. (A few other civil remedies exist, which are less often used; for example, if A publishes a defamatory statement about B, A may be required to print a retraction.) In the context of health care "tort reform" discussions and proposals, the "tort" referred to is generally *malpractice* (see also *negligence*). See *tort reform.*

tort reform: A change in the way in which individuals who are "harmed" by the health care system may be compensated. In the U.S., patients injured through *malpractice* or otherwise generally file a lawsuit seeking damages; such suits themselves cost a great deal, take up a lot of time and resources, and may result in enormous sums to the patient. It has been suggested that alternatives might be more fair, result in faster (and often more useful) settlements, and save money. Tort reform is sometimes, in the health care context, referred to as "malpractice reform," although it is not necessarily limited to malpractice cases. See also *alternative dispute resolution, patients' compensation* (under *compensation*), and *organizational liability* (under *liability (1)*).

TPA: See *third party administrator.*

TPR: See *third party reimbursement* under *reimbursement*.

TQM: See *total quality management* under *quality management*.

transfer: The formal shifting of responsibility for the care of a patient from one physician to another, from one institution to another, or from one unit of the hospital to another. There are specific Medicare payment implications depending on the type of transfer.

transitional care: A term covering care which is not *acute care* and not *long-term care*. "Transitional care" includes care in postacute convalescence, rehabilitation, and psychiatric care, whether given within acute or long-term care facilities, or in separate programs or facilities.

treatment: A term which, when used in "treatment of the patient," means any or all elements of the care of the patient for the correction or relief of the patient's problem. When used in a phrase such as "antibiotic treatment," the term means a specific method or technique. Also called therapy.

Treatment will be specifically defined in health care legislation. For example, under *HR 3222*, it includes " . . . any health care intervention undertaken, with respect to a specific indication, to improve, maintain, or stabilize a health outcome or to prevent or mitigate an adverse change in a health outcome."

extraordinary treatment: Medical treatment or care which does not offer a reasonable hope of benefit to the patient, or which cannot be accomplished without excessive pain, expense, or other great burden. The decision whether to provide extraordinary treatment is basically an ethical determination; also, whether treatment is "extraordinary" can only be determined in relation to the condition of the patient and the prognosis. Sometimes called "heroic measures" or "heroics."

investigational treatment: Under *HR 3222* and *HR 3704*, " . . . a treatment for which there is not sufficient evidence to determine the health outcome of the treatment compared with the best available alternative treatment (or with no treatment if there is no alternative treatment).

not investigational treatment: Under *HR 3222*, "there must be sufficient evidence on which to base conclusions about the existence and magnitude of the change in health outcome resulting from the treatment or diagnostic procedure compared with the best available alternative (or with no treatment or diagnostic procedure if no alternative treatment or procedure is available).

Tringa: "A sandpiper," from the Greek "tryngas." A genus in the sandpiper bird family. Tringa includes the Greater and Lesser Yellowlegs.

U

UCDS: See *Uniform Clinical Data Set.*

UEHB: See *Uniform Effective Health Benefits* under *benefit package.*

UIN: See *unique identifier number.*

unbundling: Selling individual components of a service or product separately rather than as a package. Sometimes unbundling is done for the convenience of the customer, but often it is done in order to sell the same components for a greater total price than if they were packaged together (bundled). For example, a complete automobile can be purchased for far less than its parts. In health care, the care of a fracture, for example, may be priced to include the diagnosis, treatment, and aftercare as single package (bundled); alternatively, diagnosis, setting of the fracture, applying the cast, removing the cast, and other services may be priced individually (unbundled).

uncompensated care: Care for which no payment is expected or no charge is made.

underwriting (1): Assuming the risk of buying a new issue of securities directly from a corporation or government entity, and then reselling them to the public.

negotiated underwriting: A private sale of bonds by their issuer as contrasted with advertisement for public bids. Most hospital bond underwritings are negotiated because of special marketing considerations.

underwriting (2): In insurance usage, means assuming the risk of loss in exchange for an amount of money (the premium).

medical underwriting: A practice by health care insurers of deciding who needs coverage and then denying it to them. The insurer uses the health status of groups and individuals to determine the rates, and whether to provide health care coverage and under what conditions.

uniform benefit package: See *standard benefit package* under *benefit package.*

Uniform Effective Health Benefits (UEHB): See *benefit package.*

Uniform Hospital Discharge Data Set (UHDDS): See *data set.*

unique identifier number (UIN): Under the *Health Security Act (HSA)*, an unique number to identify an individual covered under the Act. This number would be one item of information carried in electronic form on the *health security card (HSC)*.

universal coverage, universal insurance coverage: See *coverage.*

upcoding: Changing the *coding* of a patient's diagnoses (and perhaps operations) in order to obtain a higher payment for the services rendered. More
accurately called "upclassifying"; see *classification (2).*

UR: See *utilization review* under *review.*

urgent: A term that, in regard to a patient's condition, refers to a degree of
illness which is less severe than an *emergency,* but which requires care
within a reasonably short time (more quickly than *elective* care).

V

VA: See *Veteran's Administration.*

vaginal births after cesarean section (VBAC):   A commonly computed hospital statistic.

value-added tax (VAT):   A tax imposed on goods and services at each stage
of production. The end result is similar to a sales tax, but usually produces
much more revenue because the tax is not so "visible" and therefore less
painful. It has been discussed as one method of financing health care under
health care reform.

value-added network: See *health care value-added network.*

value history: A tool which attempts to elicit the attitudes and personal
values of an individual so that someone reading the history would be able
to deduce the decisions with regard to medical care which one could expect
the individual completing the value history to make. The value history
would be used to guide others in determining the care an individual would
like to have rendered in case the individual lost his or her own decision-
making capacity. See *advance directive.*

value information: See *health care value information.*

value inventory: A statement elicited from an individual as to that person's
values with regard to living and functioning, for example, the person's
tolerance for discomfort and pain, desire for personal mobility, willingness
to be kept on life support systems, and similar matters. Value inventory
questionnaires have been developed as adjuncts to *advance directives* to
make those documents more likely to conform with the individual's own
preferences.

VAT: See *value-added tax.*

VBAC: See *vaginal births after cesarean section.*

vector: In public health, a blood-feeding insect, such as a mosquito, which
transmits disease.

Veteran's Administration (VA): The federal agency responsible for administering health care programs and facilities for U.S. military veterans. See *Civilian Health and Medical Program of the Uniformed Services (CHAMPUS)* and *Civilian Health and Medical Program of the Veterans Administration (CHAMPVA).*

viable: Capable of being carried out or of succeeding, for example, "viable plans."

virtual organization: A group of independent business units voluntarily coming together in an ephemeral organizational structure to meet an identified market opportunity or need. Sometimes called a "shamrock organization." See *federalism.*

visit: In ordinary use a "visit" means, for example, the appearance of a patient in the emergency department or the appearance of a physician at the bedside. In health care, however, very specific definitions of "visit" are employed in calculation of statistics and in payment. Nevertheless, the use of the term "visit" is not uniform: the "visit" of a patient to an outpatient department in which a physician sees the patient, and then the patient goes to the laboratory and X-ray departments, may be considered one visit or three. Such definitions are often unique to the hospital, the departments involved, and the payment system; one must inquire as to exactly what is meant locally.

voluntary hospital system: The national aggregate of nonprofit hospitals and for-profit hospitals in the U.S. As in the case of the term "*American Hospital System,*" the voluntary hospital system is not a formal system, but a de facto one.

volunteer service credit: Under *HR 3080,* a program under which " . . . homemaker services, respite care for families, adult day care, and educational, transportation, and home-delivery services are provided . . . in return for the receipt of similar services..at such time at which such volunteers are older individuals in need of such services."

voucher: A certificate which may be exchanged for a contract for care for a given period of time under a *prepayment* plan.

  Under *HR 3704,* a such a document would be furnished to each qualified (low-income) individual or family, each calendar year, and could be submitted to a qualified health plan (defined in this Act) to be applied against the cost of the premium for the qualified health plan. The calculation of the voucher amount is prescribed in the Act.

voucher system: A system in which Medicare beneficiaries (see *beneficiary*) use *voucher*s issued by the federal government to enroll in *health care plan*s of their choice. Early in 1985 Congress enacted legislation permitting this approach to the provision of care for Medicare beneficiaries in an effort to introduce competition into the provision of health care. Under the voucher system, the beneficiary enrolls in a federally qualified health care plan, and payment is made directly to the care-providing organization in a predetermined, fixed amount in exchange for the beneficiary's voucher. Thus, the beneficiary decides which competing health care provider he or she believes will give the best services (best quality, cheapest, most accessible, or with the most desirable amenities, for example) in exchange for the voucher. The beneficiary receives the services by enrolling in a health care plan, which might be a *health care organization (HCO)*, a *health maintenance organization (HMO)*, or some other organization set up to provide all the care benefits (outpatient, hospital, home care, and so on) required of a qualified program.

W

waiver: A special permission. In health care, a common usage is exemption of a state from participating in the Medicare program under the prospective payment system (PPS) when the state has presented an alternate method of payment which the government has accepted. Similarly, Oregon has been granted a waiver of compliance with regulations as written so that it may use the *Oregon plan*. States sometimes grant waivers to hospitals to permit special usage of allied health professionals in order to permit implementation of innovative methods of health care delivery.

WC: See *workers' compensation* under *compensation*.

well-baby care: Health care services to normal babies in order to detect any problems early and to give preventive advice. This is the counterpart of prenatal care for pregnant women.

well-year: The equivalent of one completely well year of life, a measure designed to assess the benefits of health programs. The measure is used in a "General Health Policy Model (GHPM)." The well-year value is derived from measures of (1) life expectancy and (2) *health-related quality of life (HRQOL)* (see *quality of life*) during years before death. If an individual, for example, was judged to be functioning at a 60% level (as rated on the investigator's scale) for one year, he would be considered to have had 0.60 well-years of life.

wellness program: See *health promotion*.

wholistic health: A view of health as consisting of the health of the "whole" person--body, mind, and spirit. That view requires the coordinated attention to all three components by the several disciplines involved, and places major responsibility for health on the individual. Synonym(s): holistic health.

WIC: See *Women, Infants, and Children's Program*.

Women, Infants, and Children's Program (WIC): A federally funded program which provides specific food vouchers and nutrition education to "at risk" pregnant women and children five years old and under.

woodwork effect: From "coming out of the woodwork," meaning the appearance of previously unidentified problems (unmet needs) when programs for them are announced. For example, when Medicare was initiated in the mid-sixties, an unexpected number of cataract and hernia operations were performed; people who had previously lived with these problems had them corrected when funds became available. The term is currently being used particularly as long-term care programs are being considered, and it is impossible to predict the load of patients that would appear and who (themselves or their families) would demand home or institutional care.

workers' compensation (WC): See *compensation.*

Z

ZEBRA: See *Zero Balanced Reimbursement Account.*

Zero Balanced Reimbursement Account (ZEBRA): A type of health care benefit plan provided by employers who are self-insured and pay for the care as it is given. The ceiling under such a plan is typically "unlimited." The Internal Revenue Service (IRS) has ruled that funds spent for a beneficiary (here an employee) under such a plan are taxable to the beneficiary, and that the employer is liable for withholding income tax on benefits, except for those benefits which are nontaxable under federal statutes. Synonym(s): cafeteria plan.

Ordering Information

Additional copies of Slees' *Health Care Reform Terms, Second Edition*, as well as the "big book," *Health Care Terms, Second Edition*, are available from Tringa Press.

HEALTH CARE REFORM TERMS, *SECOND EDITION*
An explanatory glossary of words, phrase, & acronyms
used in today's U.S. "health care reform" movement.
By Vergil N. Slee and Debora A. Slee
Softbound, 160 pages, April 1994, $17.95, Order No. HRG2, ISBN 0-9615255-6-8

> An up-to-the-minute guide to the emerging concepts and quick-changing terminology used in today's health care reform discussions and proposals. *Revised and updated!*

HEALTH CARE TERMS, SECOND EDITION
By Vergil N. Slee and Debora A. Slee
Softbound, 456 pages, April 1991, $25.00, Order No. HCT2, ISBN 0-9615255-1-7

> A complete guide to terminology, acronyms, and jargon used in all aspects of health care delivery, administration, finance and reimbursement, clinical medicine and nursing (although this is not a "medical dictionary"), health care law and regulation, classification systems, statistics, medical staff organization, quality management, science and technology, and health care planning — everything an informed person needs to know to understand today's complex world of health care. Over 2600 terms explained.
> *Winner, 1992 MBA Merit Award*

Tringa Press pays the postage and handling charges on prepaid orders; if you wish us to bill you, we will add $3 for the first book and 50 cents for each additional book sent to a single address within the United States. There are additional charges for shipments outside the U.S. Please inquire about quantity discounts.

Tringa Press
P.O. Box 8181
St. Paul, MN 55108
612-222-7476